FROM SINGLE CELLS
TO PLANTS

THE WYKEHAM SCIENCE SERIES

General Editors:

PROFESSOR SIR NEVILL MOTT, F.R.S.

Emeritus Cavendish Professor of Physics
University of Cambridge

G. R. NOAKES

Formerly Senior Physics Master
Uppingham School

Biological Editor:

W. B. YAPP

Formerly Senior Lecturer
University of Birmingham

The aim of the Wykeham Science Series is to introduce the present state of the many fields of study within science to students approaching or starting their careers in University, Polytechnic, or College of Technology. Each book seeks to reinforce the link between school and higher education, and the main author, a distinguished worker or teacher in the field, is assisted by an experienced sixth form schoolmaster.

FROM SINGLE CELLS
TO PLANTS

E. Thomas,
Max-Planck Institute for Plant Genetics, Ladenburg, W. Germany

M. R. Davey,
Department of Botany, University of Nottingham, England

 WYKEHAM PUBLICATIONS (LONDON) LTD
(A MEMBER OF THE TAYLOR & FRANCIS GROUP)
LONDON AND WINCHESTER
1975

First published 1975 by Wykeham Publications (London) Ltd.

Cover illustration— Top left: Protoplasts isolated from Pisum sativum *leaf mesophyll cells* ($\times 575$). *Bottom left: Cells of* Atropa belladonna *growing in culture* ($\times 260$). *Right: A plantlet developing from a piece of callus tissue regenerated from an isolated leaf mesophyll protoplast of* Nicotiana tabacum ($\times 4$).

ISBN 0 85109 041 9 (Paper)
ISBN 0 85109 520 8 (Cloth)

Printed in Great Britain by Taylor & Francis (Printers) Ltd. Rankine Road, Basingstoke, Hants.

Distribution and Representation :

UNITED KINGDOM, EUROPE AND AFRICA
Chapman & Hall Ltd. (a member of Associated Book Publishers Ltd.), 11 North Way, Andover, Hampshire.

WESTERN HEMISPHERE
Springer-Verlag New York Inc., 175 Fifth Avenue, New York, New York 10010.

AUSTRALIA, NEW ZEALAND AND FAR EAST (EXCLUDING JAPAN)
Australia and New Zealand Book Co. Pty. Ltd., P.O. Box 459, Brookvale, N.S.W. 2100.

INDIA, BANGLADESH, SRI LANKA AND BURMA
Arnold-Heinemann Publishers (India) Pvt. Ltd., AB-9, First Floor, Safjardang Enclave, New Delhi 11016

GREECE, TURKEY, THE MIDDLE EAST (EXCLUDING ISRAEL)
Anthony Rudkin, The Old School, Speen, Aylesbury, Buckinghamshire HP17 0SL.

ALL OTHER TERRITORIES
Taylor & Francis Ltd., 10–14 Macklin Street, London, WC2B 5NF.

PREFACE

ONE of the major challenges in higher plant biology is to understand the complex events involved in the origin, development, and inter-relationships of different organs, of different tissues within organs, and of different cells within tissues. Among the experimental methods which have been developed in the urge to increase our knowledge of this vast problem is the technique of Plant Tissue Culture. In its essence, Plant Tissue Culture aims to isolate from the intact system, i.e. the whole plant, the component cells, tissues, and organs, and to grow them under carefully controlled conditions in the laboratory. In this way it is possible to study the influences to which the component parts are subjected in the whole plant.

It is not the aim of this book to provide a comprehensive account of all aspects of Plant Tissue Culture; any attempt to do so would be meaningless. Instead, the text is intended to supplement the younger scientist's knowledge of plants by providing a brief outline of the major developments in this field of botanical research, together with some of the present and future applications of this technique. Those readers who require more detailed information are referred to a list of selected reviews at the end of the book.

To our wives, Sandra and Linda, for their unfailing support and encouragement in our work

ACKNOWLEDGMENTS

WE wish to acknowledge Professor H. E. Street, D.Sc. (Botanical Laboratories, University of Leicester), for stimulating our interest in the field of plant tissue culture, and Professor E. C. Cocking, D.Sc. (Department of Botany, University of Nottingham), for introducing one of us (M.R.D.) to studies with isolated plant protoplasts. We are also grateful to Professor G. Melchers (Max-Planck-Institut für Biologie, Tübingen, W. Germany) for his advice and criticism of parts of the text, and to all the scientists who have kindly provided photographs of their work. Finally, we extend our gratitude to Frau Fischer (Max-Planck-Institut, Ladenburg) for help with some of the initial photographic work, and to Mr. B. V. Case (Department of Botany, University of Nottingham) for his expert assistance in preparing the illustrations for the final manuscript.

ORIGIN OF FIGURES

Cover illustration

Top left, right. M. R. Davey, previously unpublished.
Bottom left. From M. R. Davey. ' Growth and fine structure of cultured plant cells '. Ph.D. Thesis, University of Leicester (1970).

Chapter 1

Fig. 1.1. From E. Thomas. ' Morphogenesis and alkaloid biosynthesis in cell cultures of *Atropa belladonna* '. Ph.D. Thesis, University of Leicester (1970).
Fig. 1.2, 1.3, 1.5 *a*, 1.8. M. R. Davey, previously unpublished.
Fig. 1.4. Courtesy Dr. J. B. Power, Botany Department, University of Nottingham.
Fig. 1.5 *b*. From M. R. Davey. ' Growth and fine structure of cultured plant cells '. Ph.D. Thesis, University of Leicester (1970).
Fig. 1.6. From R. N. Konar, E. Thomas and H. E. Street. *Annals of Botany*, **36**, 249–258 (1972).
Fig. 1.7. Courtesy Professor H. W. Kohlenbach, Fachbereich Biologie, University of Frankfurt, W. Germany. Embryogenesis pictures from the studies of H. Lang and H. W. Kohlenbach.

Chapter 2

Fig. 2.1, 2.2, 2.3, 2.4. Photographs by Mr. B. V. Case, Photographic Unit, Botany Department, University of Nottingham.

Chapter 3

Fig. 3.1. M. R. Davey, previously unpublished.
Fig. 3.2. From H. E. Street and G. G. Henshaw. In *Cells and tissues in culture*. Vol. 3, 459–532. Ed.: E. N. Wilmer. Academic Press (1966). Courtesy Professor H. E. Street, Botanical Laboratories, University of Leicester.
Fig. 3.3, 3.4, 3.5, 3.6, 3.10. Courtesy Professor J. G. Torrey, Cabot Foundation, Harvard University, U.S.A.
Fig. 3.7, 3.8. Photographs of the work of the late Professor G. Morel, provided by Dr. J. Tempé, CNRA, Versailles, France.
Fig. 3.9. From studies of the late Dr. J. P. Nitsch, provided by courtesy of his wife, Dr. C. Nitsch, Laboratoire de Physiologie Pluricellulaire, Gif-sur-Yvette, France.

Chapter 4

Fig. 4.1. Courtesy Dr. I. A. Mackenzie, Botany Department, University of Nottingham.
Fig. 4.2, 4.3 *b, c, d,* 4.6 *a,* 4.7 *a, b, c, d, e, f, g, h, j, k, l, n, o, p,* 4.9. M. R. Davey, previously unpublished.
Fig. 4.3 *a.* From E. Thomas, R. N. Konar and H. E. Street. *Journal of Cell Science,* **11**, 95–109 (1972).

ix

Fig. 4.4 *a, d.* From S. B. Wilson, P. J. King and H. E. Street. *Journal of Experimental Botany,* **22,** 177–207 (1971). Courtesy of Professor H. E. Street, and by permission of the Oxford University Press, Oxford.

Fig. 4.4 *b.* Redrawn, from G. G. Henshaw, K. K. Jha, A. R. Mehta, D. J. Shakeshaft and H. E. Street. *Journal of Experimental Botany,* **17,** 362–377 (1966). Courtesy Professor H. E. Street, and by permission of the Oxford University Press, Oxford.

Fig. 4.4 *c,* 4.5, 4.6 *b, c, d,* 4.7 *l, m, q,* 4.8. From M. R. Davey. ' Growth and fine structure of cultured plant cells '. Ph.D. Thesis, University of Leicester (1970).

Fig. 4.10. Photograph by Mr. B. V. Case.

Chapter 5

Fig. 5.1, 5.2, 5.3, 5.4, 5.5, 5.6 *a, c, f.* M. R. Davey, previously unpublished.

Fig. 5.6 *b, d, e, g.* From M. R. Davey, E. Bush and J. B. Power. *Plant Science Letters,* **3,** 127–133 (1974).

Fig. 5.7, 5.8. From D. Raveh, E. Huberman and E. Galun. *In Vitro,* **9,** 216–222 (1973). Courtesy Dr. D. Raveh, Dr. E. Huberman and Professor E. Galun, Weizmann Institute of Science, Rehovot, Israel.

Chapter 6

Fig. 6.1 *a.* M. R. Davey, previously unpublished.

Fig. 6.1 *b,* 6.2, 6.4. From E. Thomas and H. E. Street. *Annals of Botany,* **34,** 657–659 (1970).

Fig. 6.3, 6.5, 6.6, 6.7. From R. N. Konar, E. Thomas and H. E. Street. *Annals of Botany,* **36,** 249–258 (1972).

Fig. 6.8. From R. N. Konar, E. Thomas and H. E. Street. *Journal of Cell Science,* **11,** 77–93 (1972).

Fig. 6.9. Courtesy Dr. S. Kochba, Volcani Institute, Israel.

Fig. 6.10. From the work of the late Professor G. Morel provided by Dr. J. Tempé, CNRA, Versailles, France.

Chapter 7

Fig. 7.1 *a.* E. Thomas, previously unpublished.

Fig. 7.1 *b.* From E. Thomas and G. Wenzel. *Zeitschrift für Pflanzenzüchtung,* **74,** 77–81 (1975).

Fig. 7.2 *a, b,* 7.4 *b.* From E. Thomas and G. Wenzel. *Naturwissenschaften,* **62.1,** 40–41 (1975).

Fig. 7.2 *c.* E. Thomas, F. Hoffmann and G. Wenzel, previously unpublished.

Fig. 7.2 *d.* From E. Thomas, F. Hoffmann and G. Wenzel. *Zeitschrift für Pflanzenzüchtung* (in the press) (1975).

Fig. 7.3. Courtsey Dr. C. Nitsch, Laboratoire de Physiologie Pluricellulaire, Gif-sur-Yvette, France.

Fig. 7.4 *a, d, e, f.* From G. Wenzel and E. Thomas. *Zeitschrift für Pflanzenzüchtung,* **72,** 89–94 (1974).

Fig. 7.4 *c.* E. Thomas and G. Wenzel, previously unpublished.

Fig. 7.5, 7.6. Courtesy Professor G. Melchers, Max-Planck Institut für Biologie, Tübingen, W. Germany.

Fig. 7.7. From G. Melchers. In *Polyploidy and Induced Mutations in Plant Breeding,* 221–231. International Atomic Energy Agency, Wien. (1974). Courtesy Professor G. Melchers.

Chapter 8

Fig. 8.1 *a, b,* 8.2. From G. Melchers and G. Labib. *Molecular and General Genetics,* **135,** 277–294 (1974). Courtesy Professor G. Melchers.

Fig. 8.1 *c.* Courtesy Professor G. Melchers.

CONTENTS

xi

Chapter 4   THE CULTURE OF PLANT CELLS

CHAPTER 1

the history and development of plant tissue culture

LIVING organisms vary greatly in their complexity, life-cycles, and modes of propagation and reproduction. Regardless of these differences, such organisms possess or have possessed during their long evolutionary history, the common feature of being represented at some stage by a single cell. Every complexity and every event occurring during their life-cycles must unfold from this single unit. The cell must therefore contain all the information necessary for the organism to grow and reproduce in its environment. In this sense the single cell can be called totipotent.

When we examine one of the higher plants which are the subject of this book, we see an array of cell types arranged in an orderly manner into tissues that perform different functions in different organs of the plant body. This complex has developed from a single totipotent cell. How are the specialized activities of the different cells, tissues and organs coordinated to achieve the functioning of the complex? What tells the fertilized egg or the meristematic cells derived from it to divide and to differentiate in a manner characteristic only of the species? Can we define these factors in terms of biochemistry and biophysics? Normally, in higher plants the ability to produce the next generation resides in the reproductive cells, and other vegetative or somatic cells have a limited life-span. The somatic cells appear to have sacrificed their totipotency to perform specialized functions within the organ in which they occur. Should we accept that during differentiation the information which was present in the first totipotent cells is completely and irreversibly altered, making these differentiated somatic cells incapable of forming another organism? Alternatively, should we consider that during the differentiation process the original information has suffered a repression or partial repression which can be removed under the appropriate conditions? Although biologists hundreds of years ago had no knowledge of the biochemistry and genetics of living systems, similar questions must have crossed their minds.

The first theoretical attempts to explain the complexity of multicellular organisms were put forward in 1838 by two German biologists, M. J. Schleiden and T. Schwann, in their cell theory. Although they realized that complex interactions must occur between different cells, tissues and organs, they suggested that each cell is an independent unit capable of forming a complete new organism. They clearly implied that differentiated cells of a multicellular organism still retain the information which was present in the first single cell, the fertilized egg. They postulated the potential totipotency of differentiated cells, a view which unknown to scientists at that time, was to lead to new realms of scientific study.

The first botanist to realize the significance of the totipotency of plant cells was G. Haberlandt, who, in 1902, enunciated ways in which this property, if it existed, could be exploited. In a translation of 1969 by A. D. Krikorian and D. L. Berquam, from the German of Haberlandt's original paper many of these views are clearly explained. Haberlandt begins " To my knowledge no systematically organized attempts to culture isolated vegetative cells from higher plants in simple nutrient solutions have been made. Yet the results of such culture experiments should give some interesting insight to the properties and potentialities which the cell as an elementary unit possesses. Moreover, it would provide information about the inter-relationships and complementary influences to which cells within a multicellular organism are exposed ". Haberlandt realized that if plant cells are totipotent it should be possible, after isolating them, to alter their environment and nutrition, and to recapitulate the developmental sequences that occur in the intact plant. He concluded by writing: " Without permitting myself to pose further questions, I believe, in conclusion, that I am not making too bold a prediction if I point to the possibility that, in this way, one could successfully cultivate artificial embryos from vegetative cells ".

More than half a century elapsed before workers were able to confirm Haberlandt's prediction. Some plant cells are indeed totipotent, and under the appropriate conditions give rise to embryo-like structures capable of developing into mature plants. In 1969 F. C. Steward, who has done much towards achieving Haberlandt's views, wrote: " One may safely assume that Haberlandt made his prophecy secure in the knowledge of many cases of apomictic development, in which distinctive cells of the plant body do give rise to embryos without the necessity of the complex apparatus of meiosis and syngamy, for he devoted much of his subsequent writing to studies of these events ".

The demonstration of totipotency now makes it a feasible proposition to seek for large and uniform populations of cells which can be converted *en masse* to roots, shoots, or embryo-like structures. Further, it might be possible to impose upon such cells the conditions to which they are subjected within the meristems of intact plants, and thereby convert them to specialized cells. Such a system would be of profound biological significance, and would provide a unique opportunity to study, in a depth never before possible, the biochemical,

2

biophysical, and structural changes occurring during many phases of plant development. The culture of tissues under aseptic (sterile) conditions to achieve these aims is the technique of plant tissue culture. The term " Tissue Culture " is normally used as a blanket term to cover the cultivation of all plant parts, whether a single cell, a group of cells, or an organ.

Although no ideal culture system yet exists, it is now possible to break a complex multicellular organism into its individual components and in some cases to regenerate healthy plants from these cells. At the same time the technique has found broader applications in plant propagation, plant breeding, plant pathology, and numerous other fields. The technique has not yet reached its full potential; fields such as somatic hybridization of sexually incompatible species, genetic engineering, and the production of rare and expensive plant products by cells in culture, are only some of the areas where research is now being focused. There are still numerous problems to overcome, but perhaps the problems facing the pioneers were even greater. For this reason the remainder of this chapter will be devoted to describing the history of plant tissue culture. In a book of this nature it is not possible to mention all the scientists who have contributed to this novel technique, and for this we apologize. However, reference to these contributors can be found in the detailed reviews cited at the end of the book.

Although Haberlandt brilliantly enunciated the advances which could be made in our knowledge if it should be possible to culture plant cells, he was unable to provide experimental evidence for his views. Haberlandt used in his studies single differentiated leaf cells of three monocotyledonous genera, namely *Erythronium*, *Ornithogalum* and *Tradescantia*. We now know that many monocotyledonous plants are difficult to culture successfully, and this is particularly so with single, non-meristematic cells. The first major steps into experimental plant tissue culture were made in 1922 by W. J. Robbins in America and by W. Kotte, a student of Haberlandt. Their approach to the subject was quite different from his. Instead of single isolated cells they used intact meristems excised from roots of grass seedlings. When transferred to a liquid culture medium composed of inorganic salts and glucose the excised root tips grew vigorously, and gave rise to small root systems sometimes bearing laterals. Unfortunately, the growth of these roots rapidly declined in culture, and virtually ceased, even if meristems were excised and transferred to fresh medium (similar techniques had been successful with animal tissue cultures). The cultural conditions clearly did not permit continuous growth. However, these studies laid the foundation of plant tissue culture as it exists today. In these pioneering studies it was evident that to achieve the successful growth

3

of a culture it was necessary to exclude contaminating micro-organisms. It was realized that these, such as algae, fungi, and bacteria, rapidly multiply in nutrient media, competing with the cultured material for nutrients, producing harmful toxins, or completely overgrowing the higher plant cells. Their exclusion from cultures by stringent aseptic technique (see Chapter 2) may seem to many as rather tedious and unnecessary, but the presence of even a single undetected contaminant in a culture can later lead to catastrophic consequences, particularly where sophisticated and time-consuming culture methods are in use.

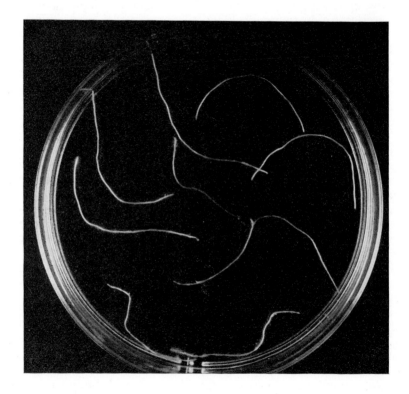

Fig. 1.1. Excised roots of *Atropa belladonna* growing in liquid medium. (Roots placed in 90 mm petri dish for photography.)

The first successful cultures were those of P. R. White (1934), who isolated and grew for prolonged periods excised root tips of tomato (*Lycopersicon esculentum*) in a liquid medium containing inorganic salts, yeast extract, and sucrose. Shortly afterwards he showed that yeast extract could be replaced by three vitamins

4

of the B-group—thiamine, pyridoxine, and niacin (nicotinic acid). Since then excised root cultures have been established from numerous other plant species (fig. 1.1; see also fig. 3.1). The culture of shoots, intact embryos, leaves, and other plant structures quickly followed. Such cultures have provided information which aids in understanding the physiology of isolated plant parts and their inter-relationship with the intact plant. Additionally, the technique of shoot meristem culture provides a means of freeing plants from virus infections which can substantially reduce the quality and potential yield of many of our important crops. Furthermore, through the use of organ cultures, methods have been developed for the rapid propagation of valuable plants that do not breed true to type from seed, or of those that may be sterile and incapable of seed production.

At the same time as excised root cultures were being established, R. J. Gautheret in France succeeded in promoting the development of wound tissue or callus from excised cambial tissue of goat willow (*Salix caprea*) and other woody species. Subsequently, he was able to enhance growth of willow callus by incorporating White's three vitamins into the culture medium, together with the auxin indolylacetic acid (IAA) newly discovered by F. W. Went and K. V. Thimann (1937). In 1939, by extending earlier work by P. Nobécourt on the proliferation of root explants of carrot (*Daucus carota*), he established the first callus culture capable of potentially unlimited growth. These callus cultures were composed mainly of vacuolated parenchymatous cells with centres of intensive meristematic activity. They could be maintained in culture on a medium made semi-solid with agar, simply by transferring portions of the callus to fresh medium at regular intervals of four to six weeks. Under these conditions the tissues continued to proliferate (fig. 1.2).

The first successes in growing callus tissues were not achieved with single cells, but with explants containing large numbers of cells. In addition, the explants contained meristematic cambial cells, which is a long way from achieving the growth of differentiated cells as envisaged by Haberlandt. At this point it is relevant to quote Haberlandt's original paper. He wrote: " To culture together in hanging drops vegetative cells and pollen tubes; perhaps the latter would induce the former to divide. Not only pollen tubes could be utilised to induce division in vegetative cells. One could also add to the nutrient solutions used an extract from vegetative apices, or else culture the cells from such apices. One might also consider utilising embryo sac fluids ".

Even at that time, Haberlandt believed the growth of plant cells was controlled by hormones which should be present in complex extracts and in solutions which normally nurtured developing zygotic embryos. The first positive evidence of the presence of

5

growth-promoting factors in such solutions came from studies on zygotic embryos of thorn-apple (*Datura stramonium*). In 1941 J. van Overbeek, M. E. Conklin, and A. F. Blakeslee demonstrated that coconut milk, which normally nourishes the developing coconut embryo, provided factors which would encourage the growth of young, excised *Datura* embryos. Following this evidence, S. M. Caplin and F. C. Steward (1948) demonstrated a pronounced effect of coconut

Fig. 1.2. Callus tissue of *Daucus carota* growing on agar medium in a 100 cm³ Erlenmeyer flask.

milk on the growth of differentiated (non-cambial) cells isolated from carrot roots. In later studies these workers used coconut milk in combination with synthetic auxins such as 2,4-dichlorophen-oxyacetic acid (2,4-D), and were able to promote the division of cells in species which had previously been difficult to grow. Studies with complexes such as coconut milk were to prove more important than these initial experiments suggested. They were to lead to the identification of another class of plant growth hormones, and to the discovery of the totipotency of somatic cells of the plant body.

6

F. Skoog in 1954 attempted to culture a wound callus which had formed on cut pieces of stem of tobacco (*Nicotiana tabacum*). On transfer to a culture medium containing auxin, the callus remained active for some time but failed to grow. Addition of complexes such as coconut milk, yeast extract, or an old sample of deoxyribonucleic acid (DNA) from herring sperm, did, however, promote active growth of the tissue. Attempts were made to determine the active constituent of the old DNA sample. Fresh DNA was inactive in promoting growth, but could be activated by autoclaving in mildly acid solution. This result suggested the active constituent to be a breakdown product of DNA. In 1955 it was identified as 6-furfurylamino-purine and named kinetin by Skoog to describe its ability to initiate cell division. Kinetin-like factors were thought to act as natural growth regulators in plants, and this has since been shown to be correct. The first to be isolated was zeatin, which belongs to a class of naturally occurring plant growth hormones, the cytokinins.

The inclusion of cytokinins in culture media has made it possible to isolate callus cultures from a large number of plant species, and to induce the formation of organized structures from some of these tissues. Earlier studies by Nobécourt and White had shown that

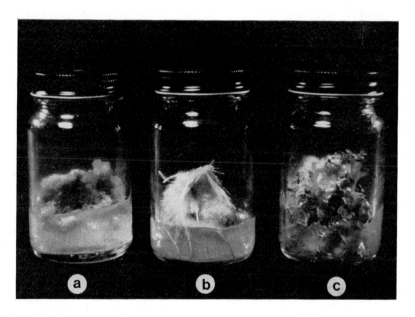

Fig. 1.3. Formation of organized structures on callus of *Nicotiana tabacum*. (*a*) Undifferentiated callus. (*b*) Root formation. (*c*) Shoot development.

roots and occasionally shoots formed on callus tissues. Using various combinations of auxin and kinetin, Skoog and C. O. Miller in 1957 were able to control more precisely the formation of roots and shoots from tobacco calluses. Thus, it was possible to induce root formation by lowering the ratio of kinetin relative to auxin, while increasing this ratio above that normally used to maintain the callus induced the formation of buds which developed into shoots (fig. 1.3). It has become possible to induce shoot formation from cultured tissues of numerous plant species, a discovery which has found application in techniques of plant propagation as well as in developmental studies.

Early in the history of the technique of plant callus culture, phloem-like cells or xylem-like elements were sometimes observed to develop in the cultures. In 1963, R. H. Wetmore and J. P. Rier induced the formation of xylem and phloem tissue by application of certain combinations of auxin and sucrose to growing calluses. In addition, the ratio of xylem to phloem tissue could be altered simply by adjusting the ratio of auxin to sucrose. In such callus tissues diffusion gradients and cell contact phenomena played a large part in determining the tissue patterns; the callus responded in a similar manner to the complex system of the higher plant. The influence of natural and synthetic growth compounds both on the growth rate and on the differentiation of roots, shoots, and specialized cell types, illustrates the value of such tissue cultures for studies in cell differentiation and organ initiation.

Callus cultures have also contributed to the study of plant diseases and to the field of cancer biology. Thus, there are certain diseases of plants in which the symptoms are the formation of tumours (fig. 1.4), groups of cells which are actively dividing but whose growth appears to be completely outside the control of the plants on which they occur. In some cases their origin is genetic, and in others bacterial or viral. These tumours can be excised from the host plants and cultured on very simple nutrient media, lacking auxins and cytokinins. They form an interesting system for studying the production of endogenous growth regulators. In a similar manner normal or non-tumorous calluses derived from healthy plants can become tumour-like or habituated in their growth. (The word ' habituated ' in this sense is an American translation of ' anergie ', first put forward by Gautheret to describe tumour-like callus cultures). In this condition they lose their dependence upon supplies of external hormone for growth. Habituation may be accompanied by a change in the morphology of the tissue and a reduction or loss of ability to undergo morphogenesis (organogenesis), i.e. the development of organized structures such as roots and shoots. However, this is not always the case, as a habituated callus obtained by Gautheret in 1946 is

8

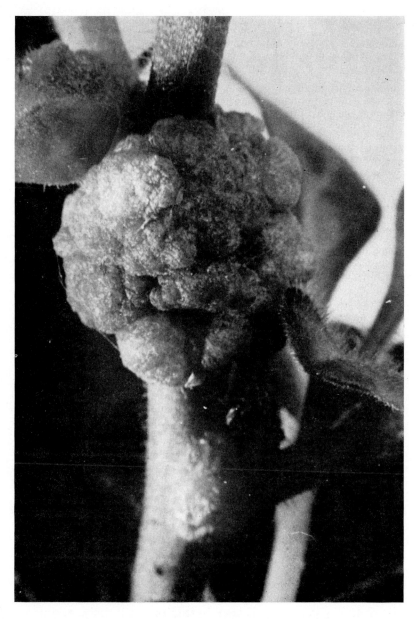

Fig. 1.4. A tumour induced by the crown gall bacterium *Agrobacterium tumefaciens* on the stem of *Petunia hybrida* (× 4).

9

B

still able to produce plants. Studies with habituated calluses and tumour tissues have been aimed at understanding the physiology and genetics of the change from normal to tumorous growth.

The cultured tissues so far described fall short of the ideal experimental system envisaged by Haberlandt, namely, a culture system in which growth of single isolated cells could be controlled. This aim proved more difficult to achieve than was at first believed. Although callus tissues could be maintained by repeated sub-culture or transfer of portions of the tissues to the surface of fresh medium, it became apparent that there was a limit to the size of callus pieces capable of growth after isolation from the parent callus. Pieces smaller than a minimum size failed to grow. Three developments in techniques have, however, taken us nearer to the culture not only of single callus cells with more stringent control of their growth, but also to the culture of single differentiated cells isolated directly from the plant body. These techniques have opened up exciting possibilities for the future, both from the scientific and the applied aspects. The first development was the study of fragments of callus tissue in agitated liquid medium—the technique of cell suspension culture. The second has involved studies on the growth of single cells and microspores (pollen grains), with the establishment of techniques for their culture on agar plates. The final development employed the technique of isolating protoplasts from cultured tissues and cells of plant organs by the use of cell-wall-degrading enzymes.

In 1954, W. H. Muir, A. C. Hildebrandt and A. J. Riker transferred fragments of callus tissue to agitated liquid medium, and succeeded in obtaining suspensions containing single cells and small cell clumps. Two years later, L. Nickell described the continuous growth of a cell suspension of a variety of French bean (*Phaseolus vulgaris*). Since then cell suspensions have been obtained for a large number of plant species (fig. 1.5). As with callus cultures, it is necessary to transfer aliquots of the growing suspensions to fresh medium at regular intervals. In some cases cell suspensions have been grown on a semi-large scale, or by a technique developed by G. Melchers and L. Bergmann in 1959 which permits prolonged culture by continuous aeration and by intermittent removal of part of the cell suspension and its replacement by fresh medium. These studies have resulted in the recent development of highly sophisticated chemostat and turbidostat systems for plant cells (see H. E. Street, 1973), the design of the culture vessels being based upon large fermenter vessels used for growing micro-organisms. Such culture systems have potential application in studies of cell division, differentiation, and the regulation of plant cell metabolism.

At about the same time as the first cell suspensions were being established, F. C. Steward was studying the behaviour of phloem

10

explants excised from carrot roots in liquid medium supplemented with coconut milk. He reported obtaining very large numbers of plantlets from his cultures. J. Reinert had also been undertaking studies on carrot calluses, and he noticed the appearance in his tissues of structures bearing a resemblance to zygotic embryos. Later, detailed studies on carrot cultures confirmed that embryogenesis was occurring. Carrot cultures are not unusual in this respect, as embryogenesis has now been demonstrated in cultured cells from a wide

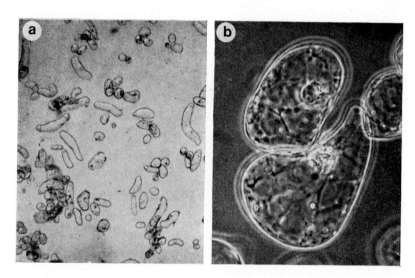

Fig. 1.5. Suspension cells derived from leaf callus of: (a) *Vigna sinensis* (×70). (b) *Atropa belladonna* (×250). Cells of (b) have prominent cytoplasmic strands.

range of angiosperms. The embryos are often referred to as embryo-like structures or embryoids, only to emphasize their origin from cell cultures. They recapitulate in a remarkable manner the development of zygotic embryos, and develop through pro-embryonal, globular, heart-shaped, and torpedo-shaped stages (fig. 1.6).

It has been a controversial point whether embryoids formed in callus and cell suspensions arise directly from single cells or by the combined development of more than one cell. Detailed studies on cultures of *Ranunculus sceleratus* (celery-leaved crowfoot) provide convincing evidence for the origin of embryoids from single cells (see Chapter 6), although contact between a group of cells appears to be necessary to provide the appropriate stimulus for a single cell to embark upon embryogenesis. In other words, populations of cells appear to provide factors over and above those present in the

11

culture medium which may be necessary for the growth of single cells. In addition, physical factors may be involved in the expression of totipotency of cultured cells. To overcome these problems it was necessary to attempt to develop methods for growing single isolated vegetative cells. The first development in this direction came about when Muir, Hildebrandt and Riker reported that it was possible to grow single cells removed from suspension cultures using a ' nurse ' tissue. They placed single cells onto the upper surface of filter

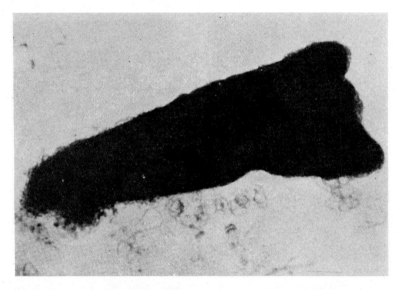

Fig. 1.6. A torpedo-shaped embryoid from a suspension culture of *Atropa belladonna* (× 1 4).

paper squares which were themselves placed on top of an actively growing callus (paper raft technique). Nutrients and growth factors from the growing nurse callus diffused through the filter paper and enabled the single cells to grow into a callus mass.

An important advance in the culture of single cells was made in 1960 when Bergmann showed that it was possible to obtain suspensions with a high proportion of single cells using a simple filtration technique to remove the larger cell aggregates. The single cells could be mixed with agar, cultured in petri dishes, and induced to grow. In 1966 H. W. Kohlenbach showed that populations of single cells isolated by mechanical methods from the leaf mesophyll of plume poppy (*Macleaya cordata*) would grow in culture. Later it was shown that the calluses obtained from these fully differentiated leaf cells could be induced to produce embryoids (fig. 1.7).

12

Plating techniques and the ability to culture single cells provide opportunities to isolate normal and mutant single cells. The latter would assist studies on the genetic control of metabolism. In addition, it might be possible using these mutants to unleash the capacity of plant cells to synthesize large amounts of specific plant products such as gums, resins, enzymes, alkaloids, and flavourings. The production of mutants from diploid or polyploid cells is hampered by the existence of two or more alleles of the same gene (see Chapter 7). Pioneers of mutation research realized that it would be far simpler to work with

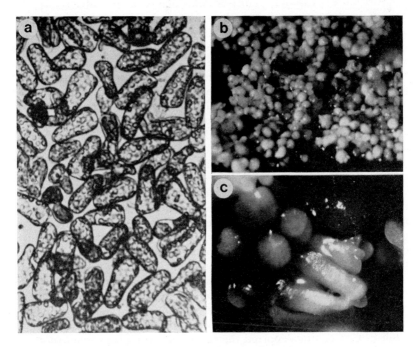

Fig. 1.7. (a) A population of single cells isolated mechanically from leaves of *Macleaya cordata* (× 60). (b) Embryogenesis in callus derived from isolated leaf cells. Many thousands of young embryoids are present in each culture (× 17). (c) Enlarged part of culture of (b) showing globular and cotyledonary embryoids (× 25).

haploid plant cells where each gene is present as a single copy. In addition, haploid plants have many uses in plant breeding. The first report of the culture of haploid tissue from angiosperms was in 1959 when Melchers and Bergmann cultivated tissue derived from the shoot of a haploid plant of snapdragon (*Antirrhinum majus*). Prior to this, studies had been confined to the culture of pollen of various gymnosperms by W. Tulecke between 1953 and 1959. However, these early studies attracted very little attention until the mid 1960s when angiosperm microspores were shown to have the remarkable capacity to bypass their normal developmental sequence and to undergo embryogenesis when cultured within the intact anther. Some of the embryoids and plantlets which developed were shown to be haploid. Haploid plantlets were first obtained from ' anther cultures ' of *Datura innoxia* by S. Guha and S. C. Maheshwari in 1966, and one year later J. P. Bourgin and J. P. Nitsch reported the production of haploid plantlets and plants from tobacco species (*Nicotiana tabacum* and *N. sylvestris*). Subsequent studies demonstrated the stage of microspore development within the anther sac to be critical in determining embryogenesis. At that time it appeared essential for the pollen to be cultured within the anther sac in order to obtain a growth response. The anther seemed to produce compounds which were required by potentially embryonic microspores. Working on this assumption, W. R. Sharp, R. S. Raskin and H. E. Sommer in 1972 attempted a nurse technique similar to the paper raft method used by Muir and his colleagues for growing single callus cells. Single microspores of tomato were cultured on filter paper in contact with intact anthers of the same species. The microspores gave rise to calluses. In the same year, C. Nitsch, the wife of J. P. Nitsch, successfully induced embryogenesis from isolated microspores of certain plants such as *Datura, Nicotiana*, and *Lycopersicon*, using a medium supplemented with an extract from embryogenic anthers. Her studies have recently resulted in the identification of some of the active constituents of anther extracts, and in the induction of microspore embryogenesis in defined medium.

The final technique to be discussed in this book is the technique of plant protoplast culture. This method makes possible the isolation of very large numbers of single, naked plant cells (protoplasts) directly from the plant (fig. 1.8), or from existing cell cultures. In 1960 E. C. Cocking reported the release of protoplasts from root cells by subjecting root tips to the action of fungal cellulase. The cells were plasmolysed using solutions of high osmotic pressure to prevent expansion and bursting of the protoplasts during enzymatic removal of their surrounding cell walls. It is interesting to note that Haberlandt concluded from experiments which had been performed on the development of sea-urchin eggs that " only a specific increase in the osmotic pressure of the fluid surrounding the egg is needed to induce development. The possibility that experiments of this kind with isolated plant cells would lead to a division of the same sort will now be examined ".

Cocking and his colleagues were able to demonstrate the regeneration of a new cell wall around protoplasts isolated from tomato fruit locule tissue. The interest of tissue culture workers in plant protoplasts was further stimulated during 1970 when T. Nagata and I. Takebe demonstrated that isolated leaf mesophyll protoplasts of tobacco would divide to form small cell colonies when cultured in liquid medium. Subsequently, during the same year Takebe, G. Labib and Melchers demonstrated that tobacco protoplasts could be cultured in agar plates by the Bergmann technique, and induced to form calluses from which plantlets could be regenerated. The number of plants which yield viable protoplasts is continually increasing, and this is an area of plant tissue culture which may provide new approaches to plant breeding and to the genetic manipulation of

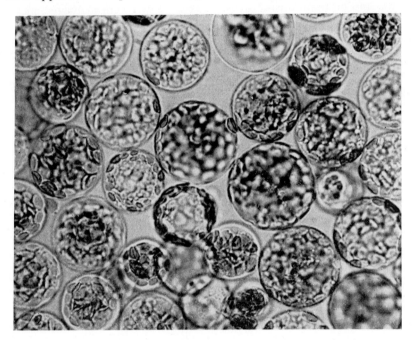

Fig. 1.8. Spherical protoplasts isolated from leaf mesophyll cells of *Pisum sativum* (× 800).

plant cells. Already it has been suggested that protoplasts may be useful for hybridizing sexually incompatible species, for introducing foreign nucleic acids or beneficial micro-organisms into plant cells, and for genetic manipulations in general. It should be possible to isolate cells directly from plant meristems or to isolate single differentiated cells of the plant body and to study in depth the morphogenetic responses which such single cells can be induced to undergo, perhaps even without the intervention of a callus phase.

15

We have briefly discussed some of the major developments in plant tissue culture techniques particularly as they relate to the postulates of Haberlandt. Demonstrations of the totipotency of cultured cells via somatic cell and pollen embryogenesis, of protoplast culture together with other refined techniques, have now made it possible to use plant cells in a manner similar to the bacterial cell systems. In combination with knowledge obtained from whole plant systems it has become possible to study biological problems in higher organisms which had previously remained inaccessible and unsolved. The conclusion to this chapter can aptly be summarized by a quotation from a recent book of H. E. Street: " We now have a new and more promising situation created by recent major technical advances and by a new approach where there is no obsession with technique for technique's sake, but a calculated recognition that these methods offer novel and powerful approaches to many major problems in plant physiology, biochemistry, and genetics ". We hope the meaning of this statement will be clearly appreciated as the reader progresses through the following chapters.

CHAPTER 2
basic materials and methods

2.1. *Introduction*

AN increasing number of workers in laboratories throughout the world are now using culture techniques to investigate physiological, biochemical and genetic problems relating to higher plants. The realization of the potential of these techniques has resulted in major advances, particularly during the last decade, in culture methods and technology, and in the spectrum of plant material being cultured.

In culture, plant cells, tissues and organs are grown *in vitro*, i.e. in isolation from the rest of the plant body. In this state they must be supplied with essential inorganic salts, organic factors (vitamins and amino acids), and usually hormones (auxins, cytokinins and gibberellins in various combinations and concentrations), essential for growth. These are provided by a culture medium. The latter must also contain a readily metabolizable sugar to act as carbon source, since even green cells become heterotrophic under *in vitro* conditions. The culture medium may be liquid, with the plant material wholly or partially immersed, or it may be made semi-solid with agar, in which case the living cells are placed on the surface or embedded within the medium. The plant material and nutrient medium are contained within some type of culture vessel, the whole constituting a culture system. The simplest culture system is an organ culture, e.g. excised roots growing in liquid medium in a suitable vessel. In this chapter only generalized techniques will be described, particularly as they relate to cell and tissue cultures. More specialized culture systems will be considered in the appropriate chapters.

Media used for higher plant cultures will also support the growth of bacteria, fungi and algae, which may overgrow the higher plant cells or inhibit their growth by release of toxic metabolic products. The successful cultivation of higher plant cells, tissues and organs therefore demands the rigorous exclusion of contaminating micro-organisms. All nutrient media, culture vessels, instruments used in handling tissues, and the plant material itself, must be contaminant-free (sterile). Good aseptic technique involves slow and painstaking procedures, with emphasis on cleanliness and efficient laboratory organization.

17

2.2. Working facilities

The facilities in any department are geared to the nature of the work, the plant material under investigation, and the number of personnel employed. In a large department the working areas are usually clearly demarcated for convenience, often as follows:

(a) A general laboratory area where workers are allocated bench space sufficient for individual requirements, and where common working surfaces and communal equipment are available.

(b) A kitchen with large sinks (some lead-lined to resist acids and alkalis), washing machines, draining areas, and hot-air cabinets or ovens for drying washed glassware.

(c) A preparation room for storage of chemicals, with bench space for preparing culture media, and autoclave facilities for sterilizing media, solutions, culture vessels and instruments.

(d) Transfer (inoculating) rooms or cabinets for aseptic manipulations.

(e) Culture rooms for incubating cultures during growth under controlled regimes of temperature, humidity and light.

(f) Instrument rooms containing balances, light microscopes, and equipment for analytical work such as electrophoresis, spectrophotometry, radioisotope studies and chromatography (gas–liquid, paper, and thin layer).

(g) An electron microscope suite.

(h) A photographic suite for processing and printing results of growing cultures recorded on film.

The essential laboratory services (electricity, water, gas, compressed air and vacuum) should be available in the working areas. Where individuals or a small group of workers are employed, some facilities may be housed in a single laboratory area. Although some research projects demand expensive and sophisticated instruments, much valuable work can be achieved using very simple apparatus. The keen student should not be discouraged from improvising his own culture facilities.

2.3. Glassware and instruments

A plentiful supply of glassware is essential. Consequently, it is difficult to compile a fully comprehensive list of vessels normally required, but the conventional glassware usually found in a well-stocked laboratory is normally suitable for culture work. Preferably it should be of Pyrex or similar boro-silicate glass. Cultures are usually grown in wide-necked Erlenmeyer flasks (25 cm³ to 1 l capacity), test tubes and screw capped tubes (up to about 25 mm in diameter), petri dishes (50, 90, or 140 mm diameter), or screw capped Universal bottles (20 cm³ capacity). Some workers routinely use pre-sterilized plastic petri dishes and Universal bottles which are disposable. The cost of conventional laboratory glassware such as Erlenmeyer flasks has resulted in screw capped glass jars (25 to 150 cm^3 capacity) becoming popular for some routine work. Baby food jars and jam jars have been used with equal success. More sophisticated glass culture vessels for specialized purposes will be described later.

Graduated vessels such as measuring cylinders, volumetric flasks, pipettes, and beakers are required for preparation of media; large flasks, bottles and polythene containers up to 5 l capacity are useful for storage of media and solutions. Flat-sided medicine bottles facilitate storage of small volumes of liquids in confined refrigerator spaces.

Particular care must be taken to ensure that glassware is clean before use. The conventional method of cleaning new or dirty glassware was to soak it in a mixture of potassium dichromate and concentrated sulphuric acid (chromic acid), followed by washing with tap, distilled, and finally double distilled water. However, the need for special protective clothing and extreme care when using this dangerous mixture has resulted in chromic acid being generally replaced by detergents. New culture vessels require ' breaking in ' before use, otherwise the glass may release substances which affect the composition of the medium or prove toxic to the tissues. Vessels should be filled with double distilled water and autoclaved at least twice (30 min intervals; 15 lb in^{-2} or $103 \cdot 4 \times 10^3$ Pa of steam pressure; 121°C) with a detergent wash between autoclavings. Washing of glassware and preparation of media require large quantities of distilled water, which should be readily available on tap from a still that can supply both single and double distilled water. Adequate dust-free storage space is essential for clean glassware.

Instruments routinely used for culture work include scalpels, spatulas, and forceps of various sizes, those with long handles (up to about 220 mm) being extremely useful. Metal cork borers and specially constructed razor cutters are used to excise plugs of tissue or explants of a definite shape or size. Large pipettes calibrated to deliver a specific volume are required in suspension culture work (see Chapter 4).

2.4. *Choice of culture media and their preparation*

Cells, tissues, and organs will only grow in culture when supplied with suitable nutrients. Media of varying composition have been prepared by different workers, and these have often been modified to stimulate the growth of a particular plant material. Such modification frequently results in considerable confusion when attempting to trace the exact origin and composition of a particular substrate. There is no single medium capable of supporting growth of all cells, tissues, and organs irrespective of their source. Consequently, the one most suitable for any particular tissue must be determined empirically by trial and error. This is further complicated by the fact that a medium supporting growth when semi-solidified with agar, may be unsuitable as a liquid for growth of the same plant material.

Irrespective of the composition or concentration of the constituents, a medium must contain inorganic macro-nutrients essential for growth. These include carbon, hydrogen, oxygen, nitrogen, phosphorus, sulphur and potassium, calcium, sodium, magnesium, and chlorine, and micro-nutrients such as iodine, boron, molybdenum, cobalt, manganese, copper, zinc and iron. Carbon is supplied as a sugar, usually sucrose. Nitrogen is most frequently provided as nitrate, although ammonium ion or organic urea are sometimes used. Iron may be chelated as ferric-sodium ethylenediamine tetra-acetate (Fe-EDTA complex). In this state it is gradually released into the culture medium as it is utilized by the living cells. The chemicals used to prepare culture media should be of the purest analytical reagent grade, although even these chemicals contain considerable amounts of micro-nutrient impurities. Vitamins, e.g. inositol, nicotinic acid, pyridoxine and thiamine, and amino acids, e.g. cysteine, glycine and casein hydrolysate (an amino acid mixture) may be included to supply organic factors. Most cultures require growth hormones, either an auxin, a cytokinin, or both. Gibberellic acid is sometimes needed. The auxins (stimulators of cell expansion) commonly used are the naturally occurring and synthetically produced indolylacetic acid, together with the synthetic auxins naphthalene-acetic acid (NAA), and 2,4-dichlorophenoxyacetic acid (2,4-D). Cytokinins (stimulators of cell division) include naturally occurring zeatin, and synthetically produced 6-furfurylaminopurine (kinetin), 2-isopentenyladenine (2,i-P), and 6-benzylaminopurine (6,BAP). The balance of hormones required to induce and maintain growth depends on the balance of endogenous growth regulators present in the organ or tissue at the time of excision from the plant. Growth requirements frequently change during culture, requiring alterations in the concentrations of growth regulators in the medium. Hormones are physiologically active in very small amounts, usually in the range 10^{-5} to 10^{-10} M.

A medium in which all the constituents and their concentrations are known is chemically defined, since it can be prepared from chemicals normally available from reputable manufacturers. Some cultures will grow only in the presence of complex additions to the medium, such as liquid endosperm (e.g. coconut milk), and yeast or malt extracts. Such media are chemically undefined, since the exact composition and concentration of growth substances in these additions are unknown.

20

It is convenient to prepare stock solutions of most media constituents at 10 or 100 times their final concentration in the medium, and to store these in conveniently sized bottles at about 4°C in a refrigerator until required. Phosphates and sulphates should be contained in separate stock solutions to avoid precipitation. Inorganic stocks may be stored for a few weeks, but growth hormones are best prepared every few days. Vitamin solutions may be deep frozen. All solutions should be visually checked for contamination by bacteria (usually a milky appearance) and fungi (wefts of mycelium) before use, and infected solutions discarded. Schedules and tables for the preparation of media suitable for the growth of cells of plants mentioned in the text of this book are given in the Appendix.

2.5. Sterilization procedures and aseptic manipulations

All media, instruments, and culture vessels must be sterilized to kill the vegetative cells, spores, or other reproductive structures of micro-organisms likely to cause contamination of cultures. The routine method of sterilization is by autoclaving under steam pressure (103.4×10^3 Pa) at 121°C. In large laboratories the autoclaves are usually of the automatic or semi-automatic electric or gas-fired horizontal type, but a domestic pressure cooker is equally effective for small volumes of media. The latter are usually autoclaved for a standard time of 15 min, although volumes of several litres contained in large vessels require longer periods to enable the centre of the liquid to reach the required temperature. Over-sterilization must be avoided as this results in degradation of media constituents and caramelization of sugars. Liquid media containing thermolabile constituents, e.g. some vitamins and urea, are sterilized by filtration through a membrane of the ' Millipore ' type. Micro-organisms are retained on the filter membrane, leaving the filtrate sterile. When thermolabile compounds are included in agar medium, they must be filter-sterilized separately, and then added to the bulk of the auto-claved medium just before it sets at about 40°C.

The sterilization time for glassware is not critical, although 15 min is usually the minimum period for autoclaving. Instruments are wrapped in aluminium foil, cellophane or brown paper, or contained in sealed metal boxes to keep them dry during sterilization. Glass-ware can also be sterilized by dry heat in an oven at 150°C for 2 to 3 h. Scalpels, spatulas and forceps are usually immersed in alcohol until required, and sterilized during use by frequent immersion in alcohol and flaming.

The external surface of plants supports a rich micro-flora which must be removed by surface sterilization before aseptic excision of organ or tissue explants. The most suitable surface sterilant, its concentration, and time of sterilization, must be determined empirically for the material under investigation. Solutions of calcium or sodium hypochlorite (which release chlorine as the active sterilant), hydrogen peroxide, bromine water, silver nitrate and mercuric chloride, have all been used. Commercially available bleach preparations containing hypochlorite such as 'Domestos' (Lever Bros. Ltd.) are useful sterilants. A 5 to 10 per cent v/v solution of 'Domestos' used for 15 to 30 min will sterilize organs of many plant species. Immersion of excised plant organs in 70 per cent v/v ethanol for about 30 s before placing in the sterilant will remove waxes from leaves and enable the surface of the material to be wetted by the sterilant. Most commercial bleach preparations contain a wetting agent, but a few drops of liquid detergent such as 'Teepol' (British Drug Houses Ltd.) will increase the efficiency of the sterilant. Sterilants must be removed by very thorough washing of the plant material with several changes of sterile distilled water.

Although micro-organisms are generally confined to the surface of plant organs, there is evidence that some plant tissues harbour micro-organisms internally. Bacteria have been reported to occur in the inter-cellular spaces of *Petunia* leaves, and they present special problems during culture as they are not removed by surface sterilization. However, their growth in nutrient media may sometimes be controlled by the use of antibiotics.

2.6. *Sterile technique*

Sterilized plant material, nutrient media, apparatus and instruments must be handled with aseptic technique. Culture work *can* be carried out on the open laboratory bench, but to reduce the possibility of contamination, manipulations are normally performed in a sterile working area in the form of a transfer room or an air-flow cabinet. The former are small rooms built within the laboratory which are sterilized internally by ultraviolet irradiation from a bactericidal lamp before work commences. Such rooms contain working surfaces and essential services, and are provided with a continuous supply of clean air filtered through a bactericidal filter. Laminar air-flow cabinets are more commonly used at the present time, as they are cheaper and easier to install (fig. 2.1). Air is forced under pressure through a filter at the rear of the cabinet and flows over a working bench at a uniform rate. The velocity of the air-flow prevents particles settling beneath the hood of the cabinet where manipulations are performed. Air-flow cabinets are constructed to give a working surface for one, two, or more persons.

2.7. *Removal of explants for callus induction*

The simplest tissue culture is a callus, composed of cells arising by the stimulation of division in a tissue portion or explant removed

Fig. 2.1. A laminar air-flow cabinet.

or excised from an organ. Explants of leaves, stems, roots, fruits, storage organs and reproductive organs of herbaceous plants, and cambial tissue of woody species have all been induced to callus when placed in contact with suitable nutrient media. The explants, if portions of stems, roots and leaves, may consist of several tissues, or they may be composed of a single tissue dissected from the plant, e.g. parenchymatous tissue from stem pith or storage organs. Callus can also be initiated from explants of organs already maintained in sterile culture, e.g. excised cultured roots. The extent of callus proliferation depends on the nature of the material, with dicotyledonous tissues generally callusing more readily than those from monocotyledons.

To induce production of callus, the surface-sterilized plant material is cut into small pieces a few mm in size, and these explants are laid upon the surface of agar solidified medium. This stage is termed inoculation.

2.8. *Incubation of inoculated media; culture facilities*

Vessels containing media inoculated with tissue explants are incubated in an air-conditioned culture room with controlled temperature

23

and humidity (fig. 2.2 a).   The most suitable temperature for callus initiation and growth is usually 25°C.   Some cultures grow best in darkness, and others under light from fluorescent tubes.   Culture rooms should therefore be equipped to provide different light/dark regimes. Laboratory incubators or cabinets constructed in a laboratory workshop (fig. 2.2 b) are suitable for small scale work.   Sophisticated culture facilities are often unnecessary, and a draught-free corner of a laboratory bench is frequently adequate for growing calluses.

Fig. 2.2.   (a) An air-conditioned culture room.   The shelves are of perforated aluminium to permit free circulation of air around the culture vessels. (b) A simple culture cabinet constructed in a laboratory workshop.

2.9. *Formation of callus tissue*

The successful induction of cell division results in the appearance of cellular masses or callus around the cut edges of an explant, the first signs of callusing being visible within a few days after inoculation. When the callus is large enough to handle it is excised from the explant and transferred or sub-cultured to new agar medium, where the cells continue to grow in close proximity to one another.   This medium normally has the same composition as that used for callus induction.   Sometimes a decline in growth may follow removal of the tissue from the original explant, which may necessitate transfer of the callus to a medium containing an altered hormone balance to compensate for any growth substances provided by the original explant.

2.10. *Maintenance of callus cultures*

A callus is grown for a certain period of time, or passage, usually lasting for two weeks to about three months. At the end of this time it will have reached an optimum size, and growth declines as a result of the depletion of nutrients or dehydration of the medium, the build-up of toxic metabolic products, or oxygen starvation of the central cells of the tissue. The callus is then dissected into a number of pieces or inocula, which are transferred to fresh medium and allowed to grow. The procedure is again repeated. Each sub-culture or passage increases the amount of cellular material, so that a large bulk of callus can be produced from a single explant.

Calluses differ in their growth rates, morphology, and texture (see Chapter 4). Soft, friable calluses are readily dissected with a spatula at the end of a culture period; hard calluses must be cut with a scalpel. Only healthy tissue is transferred to fresh medium to maintain growth. Any brown or necrotic tissue is discarded as this is a sign of localized cell death which soon spreads throughout the callus.

2.11. *Culture of tissues in liquid media*

Agar medium is normally used for the routine maintenance of cultures to provide a stock or bank of tissue for experimental purposes. However, agar solidified medium presents several disadvantages in some experimental work. As only the base of the callus is in contact with the medium, diffusion gradients of nutrients and gases probably exist in the tissue to produce different rates of growth or senescence in different regions of the callus. Furthermore, the agar itself may release undefined chemicals into the medium which are of particular disadvantage in experiments on mineral nutrition.

Attempts have been made to nurture cells with liquid media. In the early work, the tissue was supported above the liquid meniscus on a support or wick of ashless filter paper. J. Heller and R. J. Gautheret (1949) used paper wicks placed in vertical culture tubes, while P. R. White (1953) inclined his tubes. In both cases the callus remained as a mass resting on the surface of the filter. Methods employing stationary liquid media such as these still have distinct limitations, as the nutrients are obtained through the base of the callus in the same way as tissues on agar media. This nutrient diffusion

25

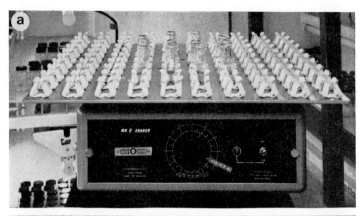

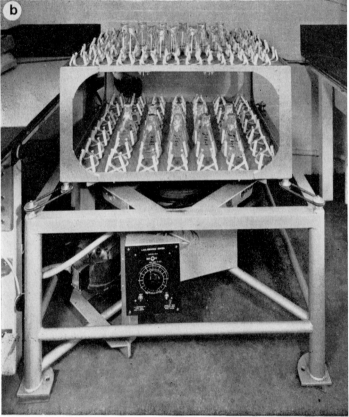

Fig. 2.3. (*a*) A platform shaker with clips for 25 cm³ culture flasks. (*b*) A two-tier platform shaker with clips for 250 cm³ and 500 cm³ flasks.

problem has been overcome by immersing callus cells in the liquid culture medium. The problem now becomes one of achieving adequate aeration, since cells which are allowed to sink to the bottom of media more than a few mm in depth rapidly die from oxygen starvation. The culture medium must therefore be agitated. This is most easily achieved by using wide-necked Erlenmeyer flasks as culture vessels, and subjecting these to circular motion on a horizontal or platform shaker (fig. 2.3 *a, b*). Other more sophisticated pieces of apparatus are in use and will be considered later.

Shakers are fitted with clips of various sizes or non-slip rubber platforms to hold flasks from 25 cm³ to 1 l capacity, and have a variable speed control, up to about 150 r.p.m. The volume of liquid relative to the flask volume is important to produce a gentle swirling action, 20 to 25 cm³ in a 100 cm³ flask or 50 to 70 cm³ in a 250 cm³ flask being suitable. The speed of rotation for maintaining maximum growth is also important. If this is too slow the cells sink to the bottom of the liquid; if it is too fast the liquid agitation becomes uneven and the cells suffer buffetting and are thrown up around the sides of the flask just above the liquid meniscus. The best speed range for cultures in 250 cm³ flasks on a shaker with 40 mm orbital motion is 100 to 120 r.p.m.

The amount of cell-separation varies on transfer to liquid medium, and depends on the nature of the callus and its origin. Soft, friable calluses readily break up into free (single) cells and small cell aggregates, which remain suspended in the agitated medium to produce a suspension culture. Conversely, hard calluses may break into clumps which continue to grow as large callus masses, but which fail to disperse into single cells or small aggregates. The physiological conditions in suspension are different from those in agar medium. Consequently, an agar medium suitable for growth of calluses may now be unsuitable for cells in suspension, and alteration of the hormone concentrations or other medium constituents may be necessary to restore growth. The concentrations of hormones may also affect friability and cell separation in suspension, e.g. the separation of cells of leaf callus of deadly nightshade (*Atropa belladonna*) is increased if the kinetin level is reduced from 0·5 mg l⁻¹ (the concentration used for callus growth on agar medium), to 0·1 mg l⁻¹ in the presence of 2 mg l⁻¹ NAA. Raising the auxin concentration generally increases cell separation.

The initiation of a suspension culture requires a relatively large amount of callus to be transferred to liquid medium to establish the suspension (about 5 g of callus tissue in 70 cm³ of medium). The dispersed cells undergo division and the cellular material increases. Growth then slows down as nutrients in the medium become depleted, just as it does in calluses on agar medium.

27

2.12. Maintenance of suspension cultures

In order to maintain a suspension culture over a period of several passages it is necessary to transfer a portion of the cells to fresh medium every so often, e.g. at three week intervals. This is achieved by removing an aliquot of the culture and transferring it to the new medium. A 10 cm^3 aliquot is used to inoculate 50 cm^3 of medium contained in a 250 cm^3 flask, and the inoculum size altered according to the medium volume and size of the culture vessel. The aliquot is conveniently transferred with a spring-loaded pipetting unit or a disposable hypodermic syringe, both fitted with a stainless steel cannula whose bore (up to about 2 mm diameter) allows passage of single cells and small cell aggregates. A graduated glass pipette with the end removed to increase the size of the orifice can also be used. Culture vessels are closed with aluminium foil after inoculation and returned to the shaker for incubation.

The large cellular aggregates which form in some suspension cultures make pipetting difficult. These may be removed by pouring the cultures through nylon or stainless steel filters which permit only free cells and small aggregates to pass through, or by allowing the clumps to settle out of suspension before removal of the inoculum from the supernatant.

Although several grams of tissue may be used to initiate a suspension, only relatively few cells are removed as inoculum to initiate the second passage. During the second and subsequent passages the cell number increases and undergoes a distinct pattern of change or growth cycle (Chapter 4). The cultures become established such that they contain approximately the same number of cells at the end of each passage. The inocula used to initiate subsequent passages are therefore of similar size. Suspension cultures of the type described are known as batch cultures, since the cells grow in a finite volume of medium in a culture vessel which is closed except for exchange of gases and volatile metabolites.

Stocks of cell suspensions are routinely maintained in batch culture in standard Erlenmeyer flasks as already described. However, the nature of many experiments necessitates alteration in the basic design of culture vessels, several of which have been reported.

2.13. Modifications of standard Erlenmeyer flasks

These have been modified by addition of centre wells or side arms of various sizes and designs when the gas phase in the closed culture system is to be changed during growth. Two-tier vessels, such as a 100 cm^3 flask projecting through the bottom of a 250 cm^3 flask, have been used for growing two cultures in the same gaseous atmosphere.

2.14. *The Steward apparatus*

This was designed by F. C. Steward and his colleagues in 1952 and was, in fact, the first type of mechanized apparatus to be used for the culture of cells in agitated liquid medium. It just preceded the Erlenmeyer flask/horizontal shaker culture system more commonly used at the present time. The apparatus (fig. 2.4 *a*) consists of one or several circular platforms, mounted on a shaft inclined at 10 to 12° to the horizontal. The platforms slowly rotate (1 to 2 revolutions/min) and carry culture vessels of two types (fig. 2.4 *b*):

(*a*) Tumble tubes—these are closed at both ends with a side neck for introduction of the culture.

(*b*) Nipple flasks—these are flat-bottomed round flasks with several side projections or nipples.

Cells and tissue aggregates are gently agitated and aerated as the medium flows from one end of each tube to the other, or as it flows into and out of the nipples during rotation of the apparatus. The plant material often adheres to the inside of the glass at the ends of the tubes and nipples, and undergoes periodic immersion in the medium. The Steward apparatus was originally used for culturing plugs of phloem excised from carrot roots.

2.15. *Vessels for large-scale culture work*

Analytical work frequently demands the production of cells in far larger quantities than can be grown in flasks or the Steward apparatus. Vessels have been designed to accommodate several litres of culture medium.

(*a*) *Spinning vessels.*—K. C. Short, E. G. Brown and H. E. Street constructed an apparatus capable of rotating two 10 l bottles, each containing about 4·5 l of medium, at a speed of 80 to 120 r.p.m. The culture vessels are inclined at an angle of 45° to the horizontal, and the turbulence of the moving liquid keeps the cells suspended. The apparatus was built for the batch propagation of cells derived from the stem cambium of sycamore (*Acer pseudoplatanus*).

(*b*) *Culture vessels of the fermenter type.*—The culture vessels and ancillary apparatus are based upon fermenters which have been in use over several years for growing micro-organisms in large quantities. The vessels are generally cylindrical, inverted conical, or circular in shape, with inlet and outlet ports for aeration and for introduction and removal of cells and culture medium. They may be connected to automatic electronic regulating and sampling devices. Cells are suspended in the medium by rotating stirrers or forced aeration.

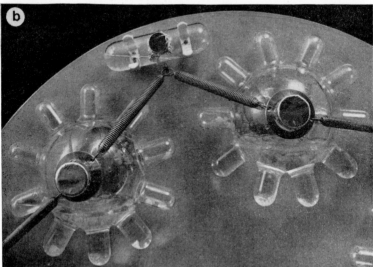

Fig. 2.4. (a) The Steward apparatus. (b) A tumble tube and two nipple flasks attached to a wheel of the Steward apparatus.

30

They can be grown by the batch propagation method in a finite volume of medium, growth ceasing when essential nutrients in the medium become depleted. The overall volume of the culture may increase as the cells multiply during batch propagation. Alternatively, cells can be grown in semi-continuous or continuous culture in fermenters, in which case they receive a continuous supply of fresh nutrients. The culture volume is normally monitored so that it remains constant.

In semi-continuous culture, the medium is periodically drained away and replaced with fresh liquid, a method which is particularly useful for maintaining cells in an actively dividing state. Continuous cultures are either of the closed or open type. In closed continuous culture, inflow of fresh medium is balanced by outflow of the same volume of old (spent) medium, and cells accumulate in the culture vessel as growth proceeds. In open continuous culture the inflow of fresh medium is balanced by outflow of the same volume of culture, i.e. old medium plus cells. Such a system can be regulated and maintained in a steady state in which the outflow rate of the cells in the spent medium equals the rate of formation of new cells by division in the main volume of the culture. Open continuous cultures can be designed as:

(i) *Chemostats*—in which growth is maintained constant by the monitored inflow of a growth-limiting nutrient.

(ii) *Turbidostats*—where the increase in turbidity resulting from cell growth causes an inflow of fresh medium. Cells are then removed in the outflow, restoring the turbidity to the pre-determined level.

More details of these highly sophisticated culture systems are beyond the scope of this book, but further information can be obtained in the book by H. E. Street (1973).

2.16. *Vessels for small-scale culture work*

It is sometimes necessary to observe microscopically the growth of individual cells in culture. Methods have been described in which cells are suspended in small droplets of medium, about 10^{-8} m^3 volume, in micro-chambers constructed on glass slides. The medium is contained beneath a cover slip in the central cavity of a depression slide, or in a chamber constructed by raising the cover slip on glass risers on a flat microscope slide. After inoculation with one or more cells, the micro-chamber is sealed with mineral oil to prevent evaporation of the medium.

31

2.17 *The measurement of growth of callus and suspension cultures*

Tissue growth results in a visible increase in size of calluses during a culture passage on agar medium, while suspensions show an increase in turbidity as the cells multiply. Growth is normally expressed quantitatively by periodically determining specific growth parameters during a culture passage. The parameters normally measured are:

(*a*) The fresh weight of recently harvested cultures, and their weight after oven drying (dry weight).

(*b*) The number of cells in a unit volume of suspension or a unit weight of callus. Harvested tissue is treated with chromium trioxide solution (4 per cent w/v) at 70°C for 2 to 15 min followed by violent agitation on a mechanical shaker to break up the cell aggregates. Separated cells are counted on a haemocytometer slide.

(*c*) The total volume occupied by cells in an aliquot of suspension culture. The cells are compacted by centrifugation, and their packed cell volume expressed as a percentage of the aliquot volume.

The above parameters can be correlated with measurements of metabolic changes during growth, such as changes in nucleic acids, protein synthesis, and respiration.

2.18 *Summary*

In this chapter we have described the basic laboratory techniques for establishing callus and cell suspension cultures in nutrient media. These culture systems are freely inter-convertible. Cells of some callus tissues disperse on transfer from agar to agitated liquid medium, and it is also possible to reverse the process. Thus, by plating suspension cells in agar medium in petri plates the free cells and small aggregates reform callus masses. The importance of this phenomena in the isolation of clones (tissue lines or strains) of single-cell origin, together with the growth characteristics of callus and suspension cells, will be discussed in detail in Chapter 4.

CHAPTER 3
the culture of plant organs

3.1. *Introduction*

COMPLEX inter-relationships are established between different organs of the higher plant body. The successful isolation and culture of a particular organ, under conditions where the normal growth pattern is exhibited, should help to define the nutrients and growth factors normally received by the organ from other parts of the plant body and from its external environment. In addition, cultured organs may be ideally suited for studying specific problems in morphogenesis, and for investigating the sites of biosynthesis of specific metabolites and growth compounds. Studies of this kind have led to important developments in agriculture and horticulture, and have also laid the foundation for the development of the techniques described in the chapters which follow.

3.2. *Excised root cultures*

3.2.1. *Methods*

The studies by P. R. White on excised roots of tomato (*Lycopersicon esculentum*) were continued in the laboratory of H. E. Street, and the culture methods employed illustrate some of the general techniques of organ culture.

For establishing root cultures, seeds are surface-sterilized and germinated on moist filter paper in sterile petri dishes at 25°C in the dark. When the seedling roots are 20 to 40 mm in length, 10 mm apical tips are excised with a scalpel or fine scissors and each transferred to 50 cm³ of liquid culture medium (see Appendix Table 1) contained in 100 cm³ wide-necked Erlenmeyer flasks. Alternatively, if large amounts of root material are required, or if large volumes of culture medium that have supported growth of roots are to be analysed, penicillin flasks containing 500 cm³ or 1 l of medium are used and inoculated with 10 to 20 root tips. Generally, the tips float just below the liquid surface, and when incubated at 25°C in the dark they grow in length, and laterals emerge from the main axis (fig. 3.1). A clone of excised roots can then be established from a single root culture by cutting the main root axis into ‘ sectors ’, each bearing four or five young laterals. These ‘ sectors ’ are transferred individually to new culture medium, where their lateral roots grow in length to produce new laterals. Apical tips of the laterals

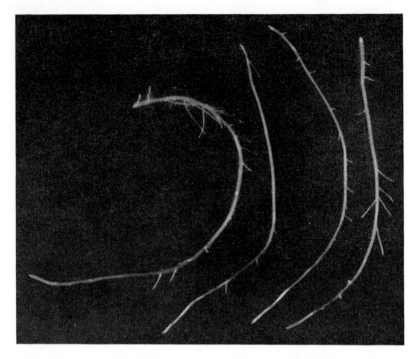

Fig. 3.1. Lateral roots emerging from the main axis of excised roots of
Lycopersicon esculentum cultured in liquid medium.

10 mm long can be excised to give cultures similar to those initiated
from the original seedling root tip.   Such root tip cultures are ideally
suited for studies of the effect of various compounds on root growth.
The 'sector' cultures are used for further propagation of the root
cultures.   The procedure is summarized diagramatically in fig. 3.2.
Growth of excised roots can be expressed in terms of fresh and dry
weight, increase in length of the main axis, number of emergent
laterals, and total length of laterals per culture.

The techniques described can only be used when the root cultures
develop laterals in regular sequence, and when the laterals grow rapidly
from 'sector' initials.   Unfortunately, for many species this does not
occur.   The technique used to establish excised root cultures of
deadly nightshade has been modified as follows.   Intact seedlings
are transferred to the surface of liquid root culture medium supplemented with 200 mg l^{-1} casamino acids (amino acids obtained by
acid hydrolysis of the milk protein casein) and 0·1 mg l^{-1} indolylacetic acid.   After incubation for 2 to 3 weeks the seedlings develop

numerous roots, and cultures are initiated by excision of 50 mm apical tips. Growth varies considerably from culture to culture, and not all the tips produce laterals. However, clones can be established by repeated excision and transfer of the main root tips or of lateral tips (when available) to new medium at intervals of three weeks.

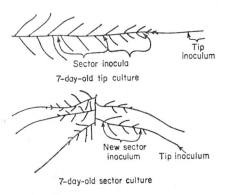

Fig. 3.2. Propagation of excised roots of *Lycopersicon esculentum* from root tip and sector inocula.

It is not an easy task to culture isolated roots of a particular species successfully, and the culture medium and incubation conditions must be carefully evaluated for the material under investigation. The roots of many species cannot be cultured. Nevertheless, studies with the successful species have contributed significantly to plant physiology, and have increased our knowledge of carbohydrate metabolism, and the role of mineral ions, vitamins, and hormones in plant growth. The cultures provide an experimental system for studying the release of metabolites from roots, while more specific applications are described below.

3.2.2. *The nodulation of roots excised from leguminous plants*

The process whereby nitrogen-fixing bacteria of the genus *Rhizobium* induce nodules on the roots of leguminous plants involves a complex physiological system which is poorly understood; root cultures provide a simplified system with which to study it. In the conventional method of culturing excised roots, the whole root surface is bathed by a medium containing inorganic salts and sucrose. When bacteria are inoculated directly into the culture medium, they utilize the carbohydrate source and proliferate to such an extent that they quickly overgrow the root material. Nitrate in the medium is required for root growth, but is inhibitory to nodulation by the

35

bacteria. In order to overcome these difficulties, M. Raggio, N. Raggio and J. G. Torrey modified the root-culture technique, and successfully induced nodulation in roots of black wax variety of kidney bean (*Phaseolus vulgaris*) and soybean (*Glycine max*). In their experiments, sucrose, and in certain cases nitrate, was supplied to the base of the root via agar in a glass vial, and the remainder of the root was allowed to make contact with an inorganic nitrate-free agar medium inoculated with *Rhizobium* (fig. 3.3 a). Under

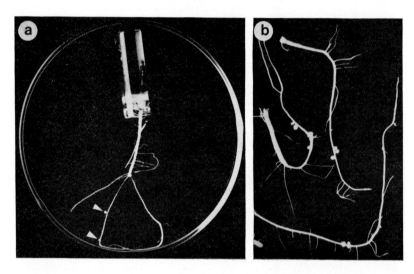

Fig. 3.3. (a) A modified root culture technique. An excised root of *Phaseolus vulgaris* is supplied with sucrose and vitamins via agar in a glass vial. The remainder of the root is in contact with an inorganic nitrate-free medium containing *Rhizobium*. Two nodules have developed on the root. Growth period = 25 days. (b) Shadow-graphs of nodulated *Phaseolus* roots obtained by a similar technique to that shown in (a), but with sand instead of agar in the petri dish.

these conditions, multiplication of the bacteria was restricted to the immediate vicinity of the root in response to root exudates. The arrangement simulated the conditions naturally occurring in the soil, and about 20 per cent of the roots developed nodules. Nodulation was increased to 75 per cent in black wax bean and to 50 per cent in soybean, simply by stimulating the development of root hairs through the use of sand or vermiculite as the substrate in place of agar (fig. 3.3 b). Culture studies such as these are fundamental in attempting to understand the relationship between symbiotic nitrogen-fixing bacteria and higher plants.

3.2.3. *The structure of roots*

The organization of cultured roots as examined by light and electron microscopy corresponds closely with that of the seedling radicle of the species, with clear differentiation into promeristem, root cap, central cylinder, cortex and epidermis. The ability to isolate and grow very small root meristems may indicate the factors which determine root anatomy in the whole plant. The tissue pattern in older regions of the roots has been suggested to affect the development of newly-formed cells at the apex. In other words, the formative influences are transmitted from mature to young cells. Although there is a large body of evidence to suggest that metabolites such as sucrose that are essential for cell division and cell expansion at the apex, are transported from the mature tissues to the apex, this hypothesis does not explain the original development of the tissue pattern in the embryonic root. As a result of his experiments with cultured roots, J. G. Torrey concluded that the vascular pattern is determined, not by inductive influences from the mature vascular tissues of the root, but by the activity of the apical meristem. In his experiments, 0·5 mm root tips of pea (*Pisum sativum*) generally developed the normal triarch arrangement of vascular tissue found in intact plants (fig. 3.4 *a*), but a proportion also showed a monarch or diarch arrangement. However, the normal arrangement was regained as the roots elongated in culture. In subsequent studies, Torrey excised the apical 0·5 mm from roots that had developed in culture. The root stump then regenerated a new apical meristem. When this meristem was allowed to arise and to elongate in the presence of 5×10^{-6} M indolylacetic acid, the roots showed a symmetrical hexarch vascular pattern (fig. 3.4 *b*). Hexarch roots transferred to auxin-free medium reverted to the original triarch pattern characteristic of seedling pea roots; roots transferred to intermediate auxin concentrations after regeneration produced pentarch or tetrarch patterns. As a result of these studies Torrey proposed " that the auxin in the medium influences the radial dimensions of the new meristem during the course of tip regeneration, resulting in a larger procambial cylinder at the level where the vascular tissue pattern is first blocked out." It was further suggested " that in intact plants the endogenous auxin, produced in the region of the root meristem, may control the dimensions of the root meristem by its action in cell division and cell enlargement and thereby indirectly the vascular tissue pattern."

Attempts have also been made to define the factors that determine the site, time of origin, and functioning of the vascular cambium. Normally, excised cultured roots show only the primary structure of the young seedling radicle. Torrey showed that excised root tips from pea seedlings gave rise to roots possessing a vascular cambium when cultured in medium containing indolylacetic acid. However,

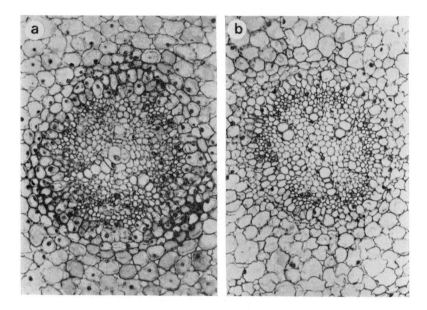

Fig. 3.4. (a) Transverse section through the base of an excised root of *Pisum sativum* near the decapitation level showing the normal triarch vascular pattern (×164). (b) Same root as (a) but with section cut approximately 2 mm more distal showing a symmetrical hexarch arrangement of vascular tissue which developed in the presence of 5×10^{-6} M IAA (×164).

root tips excised from roots grown in culture for several passages could not be induced to initiate such a cambium. These observations, also reported from the laboratory of H. E. Street, suggest that substances essential to cambium activity are depleted in culture, or that the internal distribution of growth regulators and nutrients becomes altered and this affects cambium formation. Torrey studied the phenomenon using a modification of the technique developed by Raggio and Raggio. The basal 5 mm portions of excised 15 mm-long pea roots were inserted into an agar-containing vial. The latter was then placed in a petri dish of agar medium, and the exposed 10 mm portion of the root allowed to come into contact with the medium. A well-developed cambium formed only when indolyl-acetic acid and sucrose were fed to the roots via the vial. In roots of radish (*Raphanus sativus*), R. S. Loomis and Torrey demonstrated the necessity to supply an active cytokinin such as 6-benzylamino-purine in addition to sugar and auxin. Mesoinositol further enhanced cambial activity (fig. 3.5). Unfortunately, even in these experimental systems the ability of the roots to respond on continuous sub-culture declines and is eventually lost. The studies suggest that other unknown endogenous factors are depleted during continuous maintenance of excised root cultures.

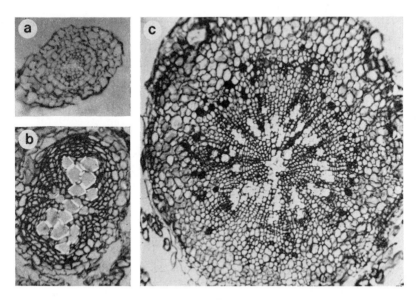

Fig. 3.5. Transverse section 10 mm from the base of 2nd passage roots of *Raphanus sativus* after 20 to 30 days in culture. Photomicrographs taken with polarized light to show birefringent secondary wall thickening of xylem elements. (*a*) Root grown in control medium showing only primary tissues ($\times$ 192). (*b*) With 10^{-5} M IAA and 100 mg l^{-1} meso-inositol (some cambial activity has occurred). (*c*) With 10^{-5} M IAA, 100 mg l^{-1} meso-inositol and 1·0 mg l^{-1} 6,BAP. Pronounced secondary thickening has taken place ($\times$ 80).

3.2.4. Shoot-bud formation from excised cultured roots

Cultures of isolated roots of most species studied can be propagated continuously for many years without regenerating new shoots. However, in a few species, e.g. deadly nightshade and field bindweed (*Convolvulus arvensis*), shoots can be induced to regenerate from the cultured roots.

Excised roots of *Atropa* maintained in the same culture medium for periods longer than the normal sub-culture period can develop at their cut basal ends a callus which can spontaneously initiate shoot buds. In recently excised root cultures, the callus becomes visible after four or five weeks incubation, and the shoot buds develop after a further one or two weeks. However, as the roots are propagated by

39

sub-culture, the period of incubation before buds appear increases, and the frequency of shoot formation declines. It has been postulated that the ability of roots to synthesize specific compounds involved in growth and morphogenesis declines as the roots are maintained by sub-culture, but does not completely disappear. The long lag which must then occur prior to shoot bud formation in the cultures may be necessary for sufficient of these compounds to accumulate. This phenomenon in *Atropa* roots is of particular interest, because cell suspensions derived from roots of different ages also demonstrate a changing morphogenetic expression. This phenomenon is further discussed in Chapter 6.

Torrey has successfully isolated a clone of bindweed roots and maintained them in culture for more than 15 years. However, their ability to produce shoot buds has not declined during this period (fig. 3.6 *a*). The shoot buds are formed in a similar manner to lateral roots, and they arise endogenously from the pericycle (fig. 3.6 *b, c*). This is unlike shoot-bud development in *Atropa* root cultures. In the bindweed system it is possible to inhibit or stimulate bud initiation by various chemical treatments, and to convert potential lateral root primordia to bud primordia and vice-versa. This phenomenon is of practical value as well as theoretical interest. Bindweed is difficult to eradicate from soils as the roots fragment into numerous pieces during cultivation, each capable of forming a new plant; excised roots may provide an experimental system with which to test the effects of herbicides on shoot bud formation, and to provide data for field trials.

3.2.5. *The site of biosynthesis of specific metabolites*

Organ cultures have been used to locate the site of synthesis of compounds formed as by-products of normal metabolism (secondary plant products). An example is provided by the synthesis of medicinally important tropane alkaloids by deadly nightshade (§ 6.2.4). Indirect evidence from grafting experiments suggested that these compounds are produced in roots. Studies aimed at determining whether actively growing callus tissues derived from stem explants of this species were capable of alkaloid biosynthesis gave negative results. When cultured on medium containing coconut milk and in the absence of naphthalene acetic acid (normally included in the maintenance medium), the calluses could be induced to initiate small numbers of roots and shoots. Alkaloids were not detected in these shoots, and unfortunately the amount of root material was inadequate for analytical studies. Root culture techniques were used to increase the amount of material for analysis. The roots initiated on the alkaloid-free calluses were excised and transferred to

40

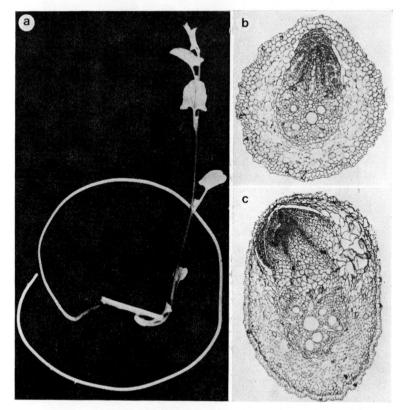

Fig. 3.6. (a) Shoot and root development from a segment excised from a cultured *Convolvulus* root. The segment was grown in liquid medium under low-intensity light. (b) and (c) Transverse sections of cultured *Convolvulus* roots showing lateral root initiation (b), and endogenous shoot-bud formation (c) (× 70).

liquid culture media. Subsequent analysis for alkaloids in these excised roots confirmed their biosynthesis by organized root tissues.

3.3. *Stem tip cultures*

In 1945 S. W. Loo reported the culture of 5 mm stem tips of asparagus seedlings on a medium containing inorganic salts and sucrose. These stem tips showed potentially unlimited growth without developing roots. They could be maintained in culture in the light by regular transfer of 5 mm stem apices to fresh medium at intervals of 5 to 23 days. However, subsequent attempts to culture excised stem apices of other angiosperms by this technique have failed. Either the stem

41

Fig. 3.7. The effect of gibberellic acid on the growth of shoot meristems of *Solanum tuberosum*. (*a*) Meristem cultured for 2 months in the absence of gibberellic acid. The base of the explant has initiated a small callus (× 3). (*b*) Meristem cultured for 2 months in the presence of 0·1 mg l⁻¹ gibberellic acid. The stem internodes are highly elongated (× 1·5).

apices have died, or they have developed roots and given rise to plantlets. The latter were obtained by E. Ball in 1946 from cultured tips of nasturtium (*Tropaeolum majus*) and wolf bean (*Lupinus albus*), which possessed the three youngest leaf primordia and some stem tissue. He used a simple nutrient medium containing inorganic salts and glucose. Attempts to culture smaller apices were unsuccessful on a simple culture medium, but shoots could be obtained from them by incorporating coconut milk and gibberellic acid into the medium. The importance of gibberellin for the growth of angiosperm apices has also been implicated by studies of G. Morel, who demonstrated that apical meristems excised from sprouting tubers of potato (*Solanum tuberosum*) and from seedlings of sunflower (*Helianthus annuus*) when cultured on a medium containing inorganic salts and glucose either failed to develop or produced a small callus before eventually dying (fig. 3.7 *a*). However, addition of gibberellic acid enabled normal growth to occur (fig. 3.7 *b*).

There have been numerous reports of the use of stem tip cultures for studying the transition from vegetative growth to flowering. B. Baldev showed that stem tips of Indian dodder (*Cuscuta reflexa*) cultured on a simple medium could be induced to flower in dark periods of 14 hours, and even when maintained in the dark. Of more applied interest is the use of stem tip cultures in plant propagation and in freeing plants from virus diseases. We shall discuss this latter application in some detail because it will give the reader some idea of the possibilities which have now evolved through the development of tissue culture techniques. The use of stem tip culture in plant propagation will be described later in Chapter 6.

Many vegetatively-propagated plants contain systemic viruses which substantially reduce their potential yield and quality. It is therefore important to produce virus-free stocks which can be multiplied for commercial release. Many plants can be freed of virus by heat treatment (thermotherapy), but for others more rigorous procedures are necessary. G. Morel showed that certain viruses could be eliminated from potato and dahlia (*Dahlia*) (fig. 3.8) by aseptic culture of stem tips. This method, combined with thermotherapy or chemotherapy has proved to be very effective in virus eradication. At Colorado State University, scientists have successfully eliminated viruses from carnation (*Dianthus* spp.) by placing actively growing plants into a thermotherapy chamber. Over a period of two weeks, the temperature is gradually raised to 38°C at 85 to 90 per cent relative humidity. The plants are maintained at this temperature for two months before being subjected to meristem culture. In this procedure the meristem (often bearing one or two leaf primordia) is excised and transferred to agar medium or to the surface of a filter paper wick moistened with liquid medium. The tips develop roots and the plantlets formed are later transferred to potting compost and kept under greenhouse conditions, which, as far as possible, are maintained free of viruses and insect vectors. Using similar techniques, virus-free plants have been obtained from gooseberry (*Ribes uva-crispa*), hop (*Humulus lupulus*), potato, rhubarb (*Rheum rhaponticum*), and strawberry (*Fragaria × ananassa*), and several other economically important plants. Some of the plants obtained by this method still contain viruses, and consequently extremely rigorous testing procedures must be adopted to detect these infected stocks. The most sensitive methods involve transfer of extracts of such plants to suitable host plants. A review of techniques in obtaining virus-free plants is given by M. Hollings (1965) and is cited in the reading list.

Fig. 3.8. Virus eradication from *Dahlia*. (*a*) Virus infected plant. (*b*) Plant after virus removal by apical meristem culture.

3.4. *Leaf cultures*

T. A. Steeves and I. M. Sussex were the first workers to realize that culture of excised leaf primordia would provide an experimental system to study the complete development of leaves under controlled environmental conditions. Most of the studies have been carried out with primordia of ferns, particularly cinnamon fern (*Osmunda cinnamonea*), although very young leaf primordia of some higher plants such as sunflower and tobacco can also be cultured. Leaf primordia require only very simple nutrient media to complete their development. Satisfactory growth can be achieved on a medium

44

consisting of a balanced mineral salt solution and a carbohydrate source (usually sucrose at 2 per cent w/v). Agar media are preferable for larger primordia, but the growth and survival of very small primordia are favoured by liquid media. Leaves are usually cultured in the light or on a dark–light cycle, since morphogenetic abnormalities arise during incubation in darkness.

Leaves grown in culture from primordial stages to maturity are normal in form, but reduced in size and often show a reduction in morphological complexity. The reduction in size is a result of decreased cell number, rather than reduced cell size. Attempts to increase the size of cultured leaves by the addition of complex substances to the media have met with only limited success.

The culture of excised leaf primordia provides the opportunity to assess the effects of various nutrients, growth factors, and changing environmental conditions on leaf development under conditions divorced from the complexities of the intact plant. Those of ferns have been used to study the formation of sporangia, and the size at which a primordium is destined to become a leaf. Steeves demonstrated that the first, youngest, visible primordium (designated P1) of *Osmunda* developed into a shoot instead of a leaf in culture. In contrast, the tenth primordium (P10) gave rise to leaves. Primordia of intermediate number (P2 to P9), showed a decreasing tendency with age to develop into leafy shoots and an increasing tendency to produce leaves. These results led workers to suggest the gradual accumulation of some unidentified leaf-forming substance or substances as the primordia develop.

3.5. *Cultures of isolated flowers and ovaries*

The culture of isolated floral buds has been used to determine the extent to which the expression of sex in flowers can be modified by the chemical environment. E. Galun, Y. Yung and A. Lang tested the effect of indolylacetic acid and gibberellin upon sex expression in the cucumber (*Cucumis sativus*). In this species there exist different genetic lines that are monoecious (with unisexual male or female flowers on the same plant), gynoecious (purely female) or hermaphrodite (bisexual). Under appropriate environmental conditions the monoecious types will produce only male (staminate) flowers, and the gynoecious types only female (pistillate) flowers. The hermaphrodite types produce bisexual flowers. Thus, the sex of a bud when attached to the plant could be predicted. Galun and his colleagues showed that indolylacetic acid added to the culture medium promoted ovary development in potentially male buds, but addition of gibberellic acid counteracted the effect of the auxin. Very young potentially male buds tended to form ovaries even in the absence of indolylacetic acid. Isolated potentially female or potentially hermaphrodite buds continued normal development, and were not significantly affected by either compound. Such culture methods are important for experimental studies on floral morphogenesis.

In a similar manner J. P. Nitsch has studied the growth and development of excised ovaries *in vitro*. He showed that excised ovaries of tomato and gherkin (*Cucumis anguria*) grow in culture, and form fruits that ripen and produce viable seeds (fig. 3.9). This development occurred on a nutrient medium containing only mineral salts and sucrose, provided the flowers had been pollinated two or more days before excision. When they were excised before pollination there was no appreciable development on a simple medium. However, addition of synthetic growth substances such as 2,4-D, 2,4,5-tri-chlorophenoxyacetic acid (2,4,5-T) and 2-naphthoxyacetic acid (NOA) caused unpollinated tomato ovaries to develop. Such systems provide a useful tool to investigate early embryo development, and aspects of fruit physiology including respiration, maturation and disease.

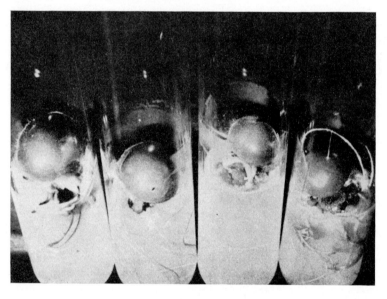

Fig. 3.9. Development of excised *Lycopersicon esculentum* ovaries in culture.

3.6. *The culture of isolated anthers*

Anther culture techniques have been used to study the process of microspore development in culture, and to produce haploid callus or

46

plantlets or both. Relatively little is known of the nature, and origin within plants, of the stimulus that initiates meiosis, and the ability to induce somatic cells to undergo this process would have far reaching effects in the fields of experimental cytology and plant breeding. Unfortunately, attempts to induce meiosis in isolated premeiotic cells in culture have been unsuccessful. However, in 1955 A. H. Sparrow, V. Pond and S. Kojan reported the behaviour in culture of anthers of *Trillium erectum* (birth-root) undergoing meiosis, and demonstrated that microsporocytes at pachytene, diplotene and diakinesis of meiotic prophase developed further within the cultured anthers to the bicellular stage. Similar studies to these led to the discovery by S. Guha and P. Maheshwari that microspores of *Datura innoxia* can bypass their normal developmental pathway and give rise to haploid embryoids. This finding is potentially so important to geneticists and plant breeders that Chapter 7 is devoted to this phenomenon.

3.7. The culture of isolated ovules and embryos
3.7.1. General
Morphologists have cultured ovules in an attempt to study the process of fertilization, and immature embryos in an attempt to define in chemical terms the environment of the zygote and developing embryo. J. G. Torrey has pointed out that the ideal system for study would be one where it is possible to isolate large numbers of unfertilized eggs, to fertilize them *in vitro*, and then to study their development into embryos and plantlets. Unfortunately, the eggs of higher plants are difficult to isolate since they are enclosed by the ovular tissues. In addition, their fertilization is achieved by complicated mechanisms. The recent finding that large numbers of embryos can be obtained from the single-celled pollen grains of some higher plants (Chapter 7), suggests that it may be easier to study embryogenic pollen than isolated eggs. However, studies on the culture of isolated ovules and immature plant embryos have led to the development of techniques which are of significance in plant breeding, and consequently will be discussed in some detail.

3.7.2. Culture of isolated ovules
Workers at Delhi University in India have isolated ripe pollen and ovules of the opium poppy (*Papaver somniferum*) and have cultured them together. They were able to observe all the stages from pollen germination, through fertilization to the development of mature seeds. The significance for plant breeders of such a technique when it is applied to plants of economic importance lies in the possibility of overcoming barriers to fertilization imposed by the stigma. These workers and workers in other countries have also studied the behaviour

in culture of excised *Citrus* ovules, e.g. those of the orange (*C. sinensis*). It has been shown that various parts of the ovule, such as the nucellus, are capable of forming a callus which gives rise to embryo-like structures in very large numbers. Such techniques are of practical value in plant propagation and breeding (see Chapter 6).

3.7.3. *Embryo culture*

One of the most-studied dicotyledonous embryos is that of the shepherd's purse (*Capsella bursa-pastoris*), which can be successfully cultured when isolated at the globular stage. V. Raghavan and J. G. Torrey achieved this by increasing the sucrose content of the culture medium to 12 to 18 per cent w/v, by using high levels of inorganic salts, or by the addition of indolylacetic acid, kinetin and adenine. Although they succeeded also in isolating very small embryos at the 4 to 8 celled stages (Fig. 3.10), they were unable to culture this very young material. Embryos are nourished and protected by the endosperm and nucellus during their early development in the plant. Consequently, studies of the compounds provided by these tissues to the developing zygote should aid in successfully culturing even the smallest plant embryo. Studies such as these led F. C. Steward to

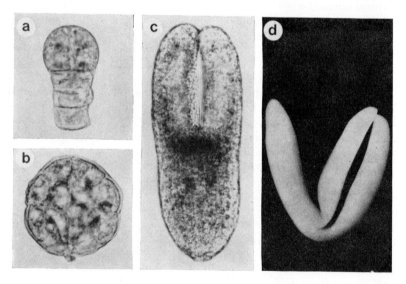

Fig. 3.10. Some of the stages of development of zygotic embryos of *Capsella bursa-pastoris*. (*a*) 4 celled stage (25 μm). (*b*) Globular stage (51 μm). (*c*) Early torpedo stage (405 μm). (*d*) Inverted U-shaped stage (1636 μm). Stages (*b*), (*c*), and (*d*) have been successfully cultured to give plantlets.

include the liquid endosperm of coconut in culture media. This in turn led to the discovery that somatic plant cells are capable of prolific embryo formation.

In nature, the frequent failure to grow embryos formed from some sexual crosses may be due to breakdown in the development of the endosperm, or to incompatibility between the embryo and its nutritive endosperm. Embryo culture has been used for raising plants from such crosses in *Brassica, Lilium, Linum* and *Hordeum*. The latter system is extremely interesting in another respect. K. Kasha and his colleagues working in Guelph, Canada, have demonstrated that when barley (*Hordeum vulgare*) as the egg parent is crossed with a wild barley species (*H. bulbosum*) as the pollen parent, fertilization is achieved and the zygote begins to develop. The chromosomes from the *bulbosum* parent are then eliminated, resulting in the formation of a haploid embryo of the *vulgare* type. The haploid seeds which develop do not germinate because the endosperm degenerates. However, when the embryos are excised and cultured *in vitro*, they give rise to haploid plantlets of *Hordeum vulgare*. In Chapter 7 the value of such haploid plants to breeding programmes will be discussed.

3.8. *Summary*

We have briefly described how the culture of various plant parts has been used to study numerous problems in plant development which otherwise would have remained inaccessible to experimentation. This is particularly true of the roots of intact plants, which are difficult to investigate when buried in the soil. We have seen, however, that it is possible to isolate the roots from the intact system, and to induce them to express patterns of development similar to those exhibited during normal growth, e.g. nodulation of excised legume roots in response to infection by *Rhizobium*, and secondary growth. The other systems described in this chapter, namely cultures of shoot-tips, leaves, and flower parts, are unlike excised root cultures because they are capable only of limited development in culture. Nevertheless, work with these systems has led to important applications of plant tissue culture in agriculture and horticulture. Furthermore, knowledge gained from this work has resulted in the development of all the novel techniques to be described in the chapters which follow. These include techniques for the isolation and culture of large populations of actively dividing cells and for inducing the formation of large numbers of embryo-like structures from such populations, techniques which have realized the remarkable prophecies of Haberlandt.

CHAPTER 4
the culture of plant cells

4.1. *Introduction*

THE organ systems described in the previous chapter were the first successful *in vitro* cultures. However, they fall short of the ideal system envisaged by Haberlandt, the culture of single vegetative cells isolated from the plant body. Application of the knowledge gained from studies with cells cultured as complex calluses and suspensions, has now enabled this aim to be achieved. Cell culture techniques have also laid the foundation for the handling of higher plant cells in a manner similar to the manipulation of micro-organisms, and have thereby led to the development of new branches of plant science. These will be discussed in due course.

4.2. *Callus cultures*
4.2.1. *Their initiation from explants*

Callus tissues are usually initiated from relatively large tissue or organ explants, after varying periods of incubation on agar-solidified culture media. Sometimes dividing cells of the vascular cambium continue their growth and proliferate into callus, but more frequently quiescent, vacuolated parenchymatous cells of the pith, cortex or mesophyll are stimulated to divide. In the latter case, highly differentiated cells at the periphery of the explant divide in response to injury during excision (a wound response), or from the influence of natural or synthetic growth hormones supplied exogenously in the culture medium, or following both conditions acting together. The cells show an increase in cytoplasmic activity, accompanied by a detectable rise in protein synthesis and respiration rate. The dividing tissue is often referred to as a wound cambium. In it, successive divisions result in the cells becoming small and cytoplasmically dense. They revert to a meristematic state, a phenomenon known as de-differentiation. The explant increases in size as new cells are formed by mitosis and cytokinesis. Later, division of the wound cambium may slow down or stop, and its activity is obliterated by the appearance of large numbers of dividing cells deeper in the explant. Cell division and cell expansion eventually result in the formation of a callus tissue over the surface and at the cut ends of the explant (fig. 4.1). When large enough to handle, this tissue is excised from

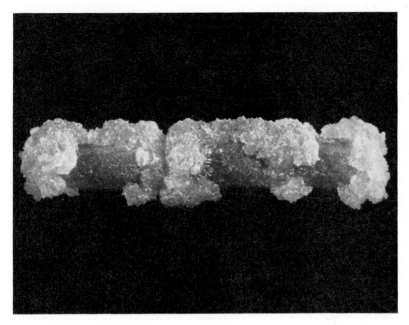

Fig. 4.1. Callus developing on a stem explant of *Chrysanthemum cinerariae-folium* (×8).

the explant and transferred to fresh medium. The callus is then maintained indefinitely by sub-culture at regular intervals as described in Chapter 2.

4.2.2. *Morphology and structure of callus tissues*

Calluses proliferate as irregular masses of tissue, and vary considerably in growth rates, appearance, and texture. Some are soft and friable, and grow as a single mass of cells, while others are compact and hard and may have a nodular appearance (fig. 4.2). Callus of onion (*Allium cepa*) produces considerable amounts of surface mucilage, giving a glistening appearance. The morphology and growth characteristics of a tissue are related to the composition of the culture medium, particularly the levels of growth hormones, the explant used to initiate the culture, and the species. Even tissues initiated from different explants of the same species may show considerable variation in morphology. Many calluses are creamy-yellow in colour, whether incubated in darkness or under diffuse light up to about 2000 lux. Others develop chlorophyll and carotenoids in plastids, e.g. deadly nightshade, *Petunia*, or anthocyanins in their vacuoles, e.g. *Haplopappus gracilis*, when cultured in the light.

51

Fig. 4.2. (*a*) Soft friable stem callus of *Cassava*. (*b*) Compact, nodular callus from the basal disc of *Allium cepa* bulb (× 4).

Light microscopy of callus sections or tissue squashes shows the cellular composition of the tissue and the location of meristematic areas. Callus of *Ranunculus sceleratus* growing on a medium with 2,4-D as the auxin source consists of peripheral meristematic cells overlying more vacuolated internal cells (fig. 4.3 *a*). In onion callus, the meristems are scattered deeper within the tissue (fig. 4.3 *b*). Cells produced by meristematic activity generally expand, become vacuolated and remain parenchymatous (fig. 4.3 *c*), but sometimes a proportion of the cells differentiate into phloem-like cells or become lignified to form xylem tracheids (fig. 4.3 *d*).

4.2.3. *Habituated callus cultures*

Most callus tissues require growth regulators to be supplied in the culture medium to induce proliferation. However, cells of well-established callus tissues sometimes undergo spontaneous change after prolonged sub-culture, which is reflected by alteration in their requirements for exogenous hormone. Such cells become habituated, and continue to grow after transfer to medium that lacks auxin, or

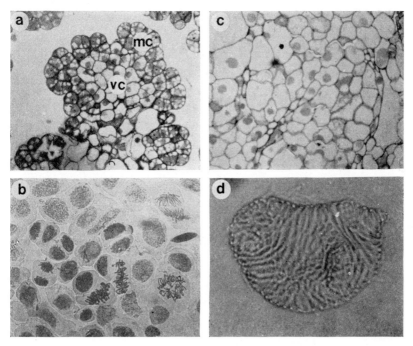

Fig. 4.3. (*a*) Section of *Ranunculus* callus showing peripheral meristematic
cells (mc) overlying vacuolated internal cells (vc) (× 130). (*b*) Squash
preparation of cells from a deep-seated meristematic area of callus of
Allium cepa. Several cells are undergoing mitosis; others have large
prominent nuclei (× 200). (*c*) Section through the periphery of
onion callus. Cells are vacuolated and nuclei are less prominent than
in meristematic cells of (*b*) (× 200). (*d*) Lignified tracheid from callus
of *Allium cepa* (× 420).

cytokinin, or both. Fully habituated tissues are those which grow
in the absence of both growth regulators. Callus cells which have
undergone this spontaneous change can often be distinguished from
hormone-requiring cells by a change in their morphology and texture
compared to the rest of the tissue. Habituated cells are themselves
able to synthesize relatively large amounts of auxins, which probably
accounts for their independence of exogenously supplied hormones.
The cause of habituation is not known, but there are suggestions
that it may be related to enzymatic alterations that cause changes in
metabolic and nutritional requirements, or to genetic changes, such
as somatic mutation and increased ploidy, that affect auxin-regulating
systems.

4.2.4. *Tumour tissues*

Higher plants sometimes develop unorganized growths, particularly on their stems but also on leaves and roots. These callus-like tissue masses or tumours arise by stimulation of cell division in fully differentiated cells. Tumour diseases are of three types:-

(*a*) Crown gall disease caused by the bacterium *Agrobacterium tumefaciens.*

(*b*) Wound tumour disease induced by the virus *Aureogenus magnivena* and transmitted by leaf hopper insects.

(*c*) Genetic tumour diseases on certain inter-specific plant hybrids within the genera *Brassica, Bryophyllum, Lilium, Lycopersicon* and *Nicotiana.*

The tumours can be isolated from the host plant and cultured aseptically. In culture they resemble fully habituated callus tissues in being capable of growing on simple hormone-free media, but differ from habituated tissues in their mode of origin. Unlike habituated tissues they do not arise spontaneously, but require an inducing agent, as in crown gall and wound tumour diseases, or the expression of a genetic factor controlling tumour development in susceptible hybrids.

Wound tumours from roots of sorrel (*Rumex acetosa*) and genetic tumours from hybrid plants of *Nicotiana glauca* × *N. langsdorffii* have been transferred to culture by conventional aseptic techniques. In wound tumours, the virus remains and multiplies within the cells, but may disappear after prolonged periods in culture. Crown gall tumours are probably the most studied. During their induction, bacteria enter the tissues of the host plant through a wound, and become localized in the intercellular spaces. (This can be experimentally performed by wounding a plant and inoculating the area with a bacterial suspension). The host cells are then stimulated to divide, probably by the release of some tumour-inducing principle by the bacteria. The tumour-inducing principle has not so far been identified, although nucleic acids and viruses (phages) transmitted from the micro-organisms to the host cells may be involved. A primary tumour results, and in some cases secondary tumours, which are normally free of bacteria, may arise a short distance away. Once host cells are transformed to tumorous growth they continue to divide autonomously, and the bacteria are no longer required for proliferation. Indeed, it is necessary to free tumour cells of the inducing bacteria, otherwise the micro-organisms soon overgrow the cells in culture. This has been achieved in a number of ways. Tumour explants have been treated with antibiotics; others have been freed of bacteria by incubation at about 46°C for several days. Some regions of the tumours may be naturally free of bacteria. If small explants are removed, some of these may be sterile. Alternatively, secondary tumours can be transferred directly into culture following excision. Tumour cultures provide an experimental system with which to investigate physiological and biochemical changes occurring during transformation of normal differentiated cells into ones capable of autonomous growth, and a system for attempting to investigate the nature of the tumour-inducing principle.

4.3. Cell suspension cultures

4.3.1. Their initiation and growth

A friable callus readily disperses on transfer to agitated liquid medium, and after two or three weeks a suspension of actively growing cells is produced. The suspension can then be propagated by regular sub-culture of an aliquot to fresh medium. After two or more passages in suspension, a culture becomes established such that the number of cells in the medium at any time after inoculation is comparable to the cell density at the same time during the preceding passage. The number of cells transferred in an accurately measured volume of inoculum also remains more or less constant at each sub-culture, and for most suspension cultures the initial cell density is about $0.5–2.5 \times 10^5$ cells per cm^3 after dilution by the fresh medium.

Suspension growth is normally followed by counting the number of cells in a standard aliquot of culture sampled at intervals during the culture passage. For most batch-propagated suspensions the plot of cell number against time shows a distinct pattern or growth curve, characterized by five phases (fig. 4.4 *a*). Inoculation is followed by a lag phase when cells in the fresh medium prepare to divide. Cells then undergo a short exponential growth phase when their rate of division is maximal, followed by a linear growth phase. Division slows down during the progressive deceleration phase. During stationary phase the number of cells in a culture remains more or less constant. This cycle is repeated when stationary phase cells are again sub-cultured to fresh medium.

Batch propagated cell suspensions of sycamore show the typical growth curve described when transferred every 21 days (fig. 4.4 *b*), but not all cell suspensions show such clearly defined five-phase growth. Cultures initiated from leaf callus of deadly nightshade commence division very soon after inoculation, so that a distinct lag phase is hardly detectable (fig. 4.4 *c*). Immediately after these cultures enter stationary phase there occurs a sharp decline in cell number, indicative of cell lysis. The cell suspension then stabilizes at a density well below the maximum reached at early stationary phase.

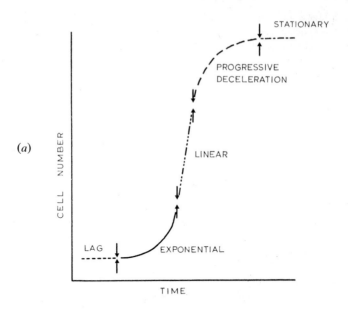

(a)

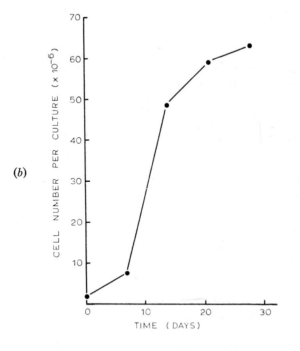

(b)

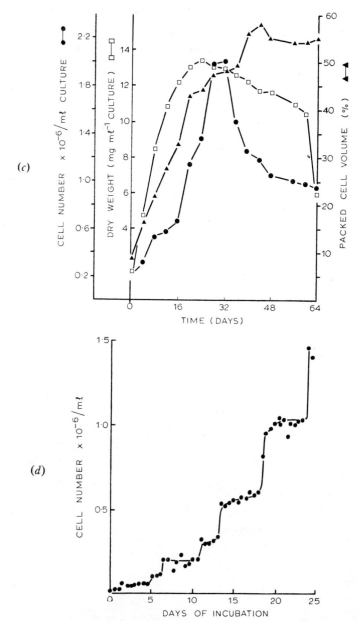

Fig. 4.4. Growth of cells in suspension culture. (*a*) Model curve showing five growth phases. (*b*) Cell number curve for *Acer* cells. (*c*) Curves of cell number, packed cell volume, and dry weight for *Atropa* cells. (*d*) Stepped curve indicating synchronous growth in a batch propagated *Acer* suspension.

57

E

Cell counts over short intervals of time indicate the growth pattern of individual cells. Thus, a step-wise rise in the curve indicates synchronous growth (fig. 4.4 *d*), in which a large proportion of the individual cells of the population enter division simultaneously. Measurements of packed cell volume and dry weight also indicate the growth characteristics of a suspension (fig. 4.4 *c*). These curves rise during the division stage as the number of cells increases, while the packed cell volume continues to increase during stationary phase as a result of cell expansion. Fresh weight of cells from suspension culture is more difficult to assess as a growth parameter because of inaccuracies resulting from carry-over of culture medium on the harvested material. Measurements of cell number and of fresh and dry weights can equally well be used to estimate growth of calluses on agar. In this case more variation may be found between cultures, so that larger numbers of replicates should be examined to ensure valid results.

4.3.2. *The morphology of cells in suspension*

Suspension cultures consist of varying proportions of cell aggregates and free (single) cells. When tissue cells are released as free cells and cultured under conditions conducive to their most rapid growth, the similarity of the growing cells derived from different species, or different tissues of the same species, becomes strikingly apparent. There is often considerable variation in the morphological appearance

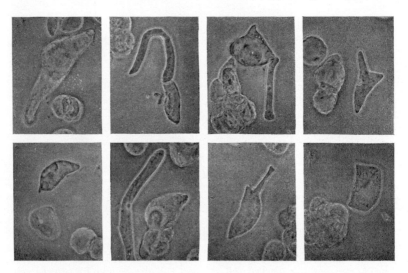

Fig. 4.5. Light micrographs showing the variation in morphological appearance of *Atropa* cells in suspension (× 125).

58

of the free cells in a single culture (fig. 4.5), and abnormal cell-shapes are often correlated with changes in the chromosome complement of the cells, such as increase in ploidy. The size and nature of the aggregates depends to some extent on the composition of the culture medium, particularly the type and concentration of growth hormones present, e.g. finely dispersed suspensions of deadly nightshade growing in culture medium containing 2 mg l^{-1} naphthaleneacetic acid become highly aggregated when cells are transferred to medium lacking this auxin.

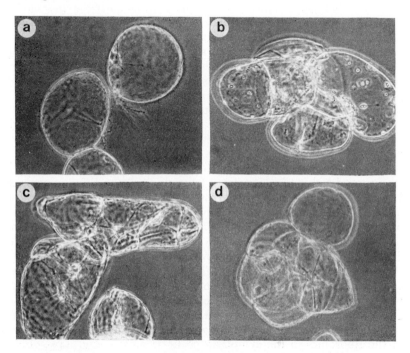

Fig. 4.6. Changes in the morphology of *Atropa* cells during their growth cycle in suspension. (*a*) Expanded stationary phase cells. (*b*) Cells four days after sub-culture showing an increase in cytoplasm and refractive plastids. (*c*) Cells eight days old with prominent cytoplasmic strands. Cells form tight aggregates or chains during this time of division. (*d*) Cells 16 days old with decreased cytoplasmic activity (× 250).

Cells undergo characteristic patterns of morphological and cyto-logical change during batch propagation, reflecting the pattern of change in the nutrient environment (fig. 4.6). Sub-culture of quiescent, stationary phase cells to fresh medium is followed by a resumption of cytoplasmic activity, and the appearance of prominent cytoplasmic strands. Movement of organelles such as mitochondria and plastids can be observed in the streaming cytoplasm of these strands by phase contrast light microscopy. Cell division then results in the formation of chains or tight aggregates of cells. Cytoplasmic activity declines as division slows down, and the cells expand and separate as they again enter stationary phase.

4.4. *Ultrastructure of callus and suspension cells*

The morphological changes observed in cells during a passage in suspension are complemented by changes in fine structure. Cells of finely dispersed suspension cultures will, within limits, all exhibit a comparable appearance in thin section when sampled at the same stage in their growth cycle. Parenchymatous cells of callus tissues show greater variation in cytoplasmic structure depending on their position in the tissue. This variation is related to gradients of nutrients and gaseous supply in the callus, which result in localized areas of cells in different states of growth. Even so, calluses still exhibit the typical sigmoid growth curve during a normal culture passage.

Cells of callus and suspension cultures show many similarities in structural detail, whether isolated from the same or different species. In stationary phase cells, most of the cell volume is occupied by the large central vacuole, and the cytoplasm forms a thin peripheral lining beneath the cell wall (fig. 4.7 *a*). The number of organelles is minimal at this stage. Transfer of the cells to fresh medium is followed by the synthesis of new cytoplasm, and a reduction in size of the central vacuole (fig. 4.7 *b*). The latter is often replaced by many smaller vacuoles. There is an increase in the extent of the endoplasmic reticulum, and in the number of mitochondria, plastids, golgi bodies, and ribosomes (fig. 4.7 *c*). The endoplasmic reticulum frequently occurs as sheets running parallel with the cell wall. Many of the ribosomes in the cytoplasm occur as polysome groups; others associate with the endoplasmic reticulum to form rough membranes. The densely staining chromatin has a scattered appearance in nuclei of interphase cells, but it condenses and becomes more prominent as cells enter division (fig. 4.7 *d*). The nuclear membrane breaks down at the beginning of mitosis (prophase), and at metaphase the chromosomes lie across the equator of the cell. Although membranes are found scattered between the chromosomes, other organelles such as mitochondria and plastids are restricted to the periphery of the cytoplasm (fig. 4.7 *e*). At cytokinesis a new cell plate develops in the cytoplasm between the daughter nuclei from the coalescence of vesicles (fig. 4.7 *f*). Their coalescence initially produces contorted membrane-bounded figures (fig. 4.7 *g*), but as development proceeds

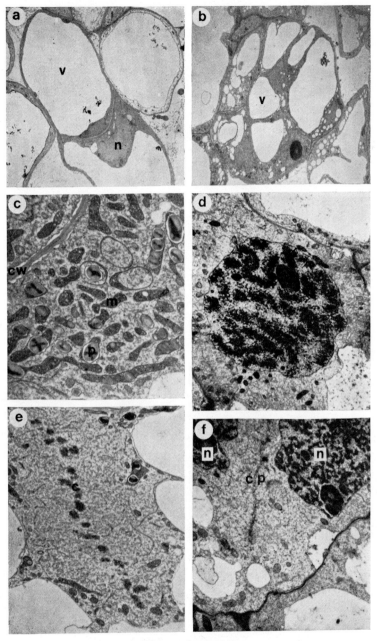

Fig. 4.7 *(see p.* 63)

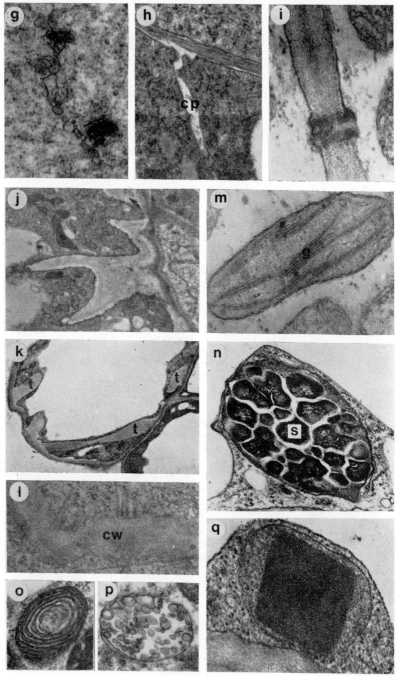

Fig. 4.7 (see opposite)

62

the membranes become aligned parallel to each other as they form the plasmalemmata of the adjacent daughter cells. The cell plate extends outwards until it joins with the parent cell wall (fig. 4.7 *h*), completing the separation of the cytoplasms of the two daughter cells. In cultured cells, the cell plate frequently joins up with one wall of the parent cell before crossing the cytoplasm and joining with the opposite wall. This is unlike the situation in dividing cells of organized meristems where development of the cell plate proceeds at equal rates from the centre of the cytoplasm towards opposite walls. The walls of parenchymatous callus cells are usually thin and pierced by plasmodesmata (fig. 4.7 *i*), which establish continuity between the cytoplasms of adjacent cells of callus tissues and suspension aggregates. Sometimes cell walls develop irregular cellulosic thickenings which project into the cytoplasm (fig. 4.7 *j*), but these are quite distinct from the regular lignified banded thickenings found on the walls of differentiating tracheids (fig. 4.7 *k*). Microtubules are associated with the walls of actively growing cells (fig. 4.7 *l*). Cells of green cultures contain chloroplasts, but generally the internal system of grana of these organelles is poorly developed (fig. 4.7 *m*). More frequently the plastids function as amyloplasts (figs. 4.7 *n*), and contain starch synthesized from carbohydrate provided in the medium. Starch often accumulates after cells are sub-cultured to fresh medium,

---

Fig. 4.7. Electron micrographs: Ultrastructure of cultured cells. (*a*) Stationary phase cells with a large central vacuole (v) and thin peripheral lining of cytoplasm. n = nucleus (× 800). (*b*) Cells four days after sub-culture. Vacuoles (v) are smaller and the cytoplasm has increased in extent. Central area of the micrograph is occupied by six cells (× 800). (*c*) Organelles in the cytoplasm of a cell four days after sub-culture. cw = cell wall; m = mitochondrion; p = plastid (× 7600). (*d*) Condensation of chromatin in the nucleus just before mitotic prophase (× 2800). (*e*) Cell in metaphase. The chromosomes (*c*) lie across the equator of the cell (× 3400). (*f*) Cytokinesis. The new cell plate (cp) is developing in the cytoplasm between the two daughter nuclei (n) (× 5000). (*g*) Contorted membrane-bounded figures of the developing cell plate (× 22 000). (*h*) Junction of the cell plate (cp) with the parent cell wall (× 20 000). (*i*) A plasmodesma connecting adjacent cells (× 55 000). (*j*) Cellulosic wall thickenings projecting into the cytoplasm (× 6000). (*k*) Regular lignified banded thickenings (t) on the wall of a developing trachery element (× 4000). (*l*) Microtubules beneath the cell wall (cw) (× 40 000). (*m*) Chloroplast from a green callus. Internal membranes are sparse and grana (g) poorly developed (× 20 000). (*n*) Starch grains (s) in an amyloplast. (× 20 000). (*o*) Myelin-like body (× 27 000). (*p*) Multivesicular body (× 20 000). (*q*) Microbody containing a crystal (× 40 000). Figs. (*a*), (*b*), (*c*), (*e*), (*j*), (*l*), (*o*), (*p*),—*Glycine max.* Figs. (*d*), (*f*), (*g*), (*h*),—*Allium cepa.* Figs. (*i*), (*m*), (*n*), (*q*),—*Atropa belladonna.* Fig. (*k*)—*Convolvulus arvensis.*

declines in amount during division as the reserves are utilized, and accumulates again as the cells enter stationary phase. Its disappearance from cells maintained in stationary phase without sub-culture coincides with depletion of nutrients in the medium. Other general features of cultured cells include the presence of membranous myelin-like bodies (fig. 4.7 o), and membrane-enclosed groups of vesicles (multivesicular bodies; fig. 4.7 p) in the cytoplasm. Microbodies containing crystals (fig. 4.7 q) are present in some cells and are generally more numerous during stationary phase.

4.5. *The heterogeneity of tissue cultures*

In the cultures so far mentioned there exists a great deal of variation and even the best cell suspensions are not suspensions of single cells but contain aggregates and single cells in varying proportions. Furthermore, studies on calluses and cell suspensions have not only demonstrated differences in texture, morphology, biochemistry, and morphogenetic potential amongst the cell types within the cultures, but they have also shown the presence of cells containing different degrees of polyploidy and various chromosomal mutations. One of the possible reasons for this heterogeneity is that the calluses or suspensions may be initiated from relatively large explants containing many different cells. The explants generally contain different cell types in different physiological states. The different cell types may also be genetically different. Thus, there is a large body of evidence suggesting that during cellular differentiation initially diploid cells present in the plant meristems can undergo changes in nuclear structure giving rise to cells with highly polyploid nuclei. It follows that if an explant containing cells in different morphological, physiological, and genetic conditions is used to establish a growing culture, the latter will also be heterogeneous and may contain growing cells of vastly different physiology and genetics, unless the conditions select for the growth of a particular cell type. Another possible reason for the heterogeneity in cultured cells arises from the observation that diploid cells in culture can give rise to cells showing abnormalities in nuclear behaviour. It has been suggested that cultured cells may be genetically unstable, or that a particular kind of cellular differentiation analogous to that observed in intact plants may occur *in vitro*. Much of the observed heterogeneity could also be due to changing physiology during culture. Until the recent development of highly sophisticated chemostats and turbidostats, suspension cells were routinely propagated in batch culture, often for prolonged periods before sub-culture. Such a technique leads to depletion of nutrients and growth factors, to the production of compounds toxic to growth, and to the development of nutrient gradients within aggregates. All these phenomena can result in heterogeneous growth.

Several workers have examined the effects produced on viability and culture growth by substantially reducing the inoculum size at sub-culture so as to produce low density cultures, and have studied also the growth of single, isolated cells. The aim of culturing cells at low density is twofold. First, it indicates differences in the growth requirements of individual cells compared to the growth requirements of large cell populations. Second, growth at low density allows interesting homogeneous cell lines or clones (cells originally derived from the same parent plant) to be selected from a large heterogeneous cell culture. Homogeneous populations are subject to less variation than heterogeneous populations, and biologically are the most meaningful for experimental studies.

4.6. Low density inocula

4.6.1. The effect on cell growth in suspension culture

The effect of cell density on culture growth is readily apparent when suspensions are inoculated over a range of cell densities. Reduction of the inoculum density causes an extension of the lag phase of growth. The division stage is also prolonged, but the final cell number achieved by the time the culture enters stationary phase is comparable to the cell number of stock cultures inoculated at the normal or high density. Eventually a stage is reached at which further reduction in inoculum density fails to give reproducible growth of the cultures, and although some replicates may grow, others may not. This stage is defined as the minimum effective cell density of the culture. A definite number of cells must therefore be transferred at each sub-culture to maintain reproducible growth of the suspension. The minimum effective cell density is related to the nature of the cell line, and to the age and incubation conditions of the suspension used as inoculum. An inoculum taken from an actively dividing stock culture will have a lower minimum effective cell density than an inoculum from a stationary phase stock culture. Similarly, a suspension containing large cell aggregates will have a lower minimum effective cell density than a very friable suspension containing a large proportion of single cells, since cell division is initiated more rapidly in cell aggregates than in free cells following transfer to fresh medium. The minimum effective cell density in synthetic medium for suspension cells derived from the vascular cambium of sycamore and sub-cultured at stationary phase is $1 \cdot 0$–$1 \cdot 5 \times 10^4$ cells per cm^3.

The failure of cells to grow reproducibly after inoculation below the minimum effective cell density indicates that the growth requirements of individual cells are physiologically more exacting in terms of nutrition than are those of a high-density population. At low densities a standard synthetic medium normally used for the routine maintenance of a suspension may be inadequate to meet the more exacting requirements of the cells. Attempts have been made to gain more understanding of these special growth requirements, and to supplement or improve culture media to stimulate cell division. Work over a number of years has shown that actively growing cells may provide some of the growth substances necessary to stimulate cells to divide in low density cultures. The experimental approaches which have led to these conclusions are summarized as follows:

4.6.1.1. *The nurse tissue effect*

In 1953 W. H. Muir first reported a promotion of division in single isolated plant cells by actively growing callus tissue. His technique employed a filter paper square or raft. The single cells were placed on the upper surface of the raft, while its lower surface rested on the top of an actively growing callus mass maintained on agar medium. The single cells received nutrients diffusing upwards through the callus tissue and filter raft from the medium below, and were stimulated to divide by growth substances synthesized by the dividing cells of the callus which also diffused through the paper raft. The callus tissue thus acted as a ' nurse tissue ' in stimulating division.

4.6.1.2. *Conditioned media*

Workers have attempted to define the growth-promoting substances responsible for the nurse effect, although positive identification of all the substances involved has not been achieved. When cells, particularly those from an actively growing suspension culture, are transferred to fresh medium at high density, they absorb nutrients from the medium but simultaneously release growth-promoting compounds into the liquid. If the cells are removed from the medium after a relatively short period of time, e.g. after 48 hours, the amount of nutrient depletion is minimal, but the medium is enhanced or ' conditioned ' with growth promoting metabolites. R. Stuart and H. E. Street developed a simple apparatus for conditioning synthetic medium used for growing sycamore cells in suspension. They contained the high density cell suspension culture (the ' nurse tissue ') in a Visking dialysis membrane or a porous Pyrex sintered thimble, which was then immersed in fresh agitated liquid medium contained in an Erlenmeyer flask. The membrane or sinter allowed diffusion of solutes from the cells into the fresh medium. Conditioning is determined by the incubation time, cell density, and volume of the high density suspension relative to the volume of fresh medium.

These variables must be determined for the suspension under investigation. The minimum effective cell density of sycamore cells can be reduced to 1.0–1.5×10^3 cells per cm^3 by using synthetic medium conditioned by actively dividing cells of the same clone. The conditioning effect may, in part, be due to the release of a complex mixture of amino acids into the medium by the cells, as similar results can be obtained with sycamore cells by using a synthetic medium containing the same complex mixture of amino acids as those identified by analysis of conditioned medium. Cross-conditioning has also been demonstrated, i.e. cells from one species may be effective in promoting growth of another species inoculated at low density.

4.6.1.3. *Gaseous factors*

The gas phase above a suspension also affects culture growth at low inoculum density. Stuart and Street also showed that a volatile factor or factors produced by an actively-growing high-density sycamore suspension would stimulate division of a low-density culture. They used a two-tier vessel (a $100 \ cm^3$ Erlenmeyer flask projecting through the bottom of a $250 \ cm^3$ flask) in which the two cells suspensions had a common gaseous atmosphere. The gaseous factors also enhanced the stimulatory effect of conditioned medium. Thus, the minimum effective cell density for sycamore suspensions can be reduced to 600 cells cm^3 in conditioned medium with the gas phase in contact with an actively growing high density suspension. The volatile substances have not been identified, although a promotive effect on low density cultures has been demonstrated by increasing the carbon dioxide level to 1 per cent v/v and by addition of 2.5 parts per million of ethylene to the gas phase.

4.6.2. *The growth of cells at low density in agar medium—the Bergmann plating technique*

Callus cultures and cell suspensions are freely inter-convertible, and in 1960 L. Bergmann demonstrated the ability of single cells from suspension cultures of tobacco (*Nicotiana tabacum* v. ' Samsun ') and bean (*Phaseolus vulgaris* v. ' Early golden cluster ') to divide and form small cell colonies when evenly dispersed within a thin layer of agar medium in a petri dish. The colonies developed into callus masses on transfer to fresh agar medium. Plating is carried out by mixing cells suspended in liquid medium with an equal volume of medium containing about 1.2 per cent w/v agar (double the final agar concentration) at a temperature of $40°C$. The mixture is immediately poured into a petri dish (about $10 \ cm^3$ final culture volume in a 90 mm dish), gently swirled to ensure even distribution of cells and allowed to stand until set. The dishes are sealed with tape. The position of individual cells can be marked on the dish and their development followed at intervals by light microscopy. The plates are generally incubated in darkness or under low-intensity diffuse light.

The number of viable cell colonies which develop on agar plates, expressed as a percentage of the original number of cells spread in the medium, gives an estimate of the plating efficiency of the cell suspension. The number of cells spread per plate is estimated by counting the number of cells in a sample from the original cell suspension before mixing with the warm agar medium. Colony number per plate is estimated by counting the cell aggregates in randomly selected areas of known dimensions. Counting can be facilitated by superimposing the negative of a suitable sized grid pattern over a shadowgraph of the plate. The plating efficiency is directly related to the inoculum density at plating (plating density), to the culture medium, and to the nature and age of the suspension. Cell aggregates, even of only a few cells, divide more rapidly than single cells. Actively dividing suspensions have a higher plating efficiency than cells plated from stationary phase cultures.

4.6.3. *Application of the Bergmann plating technique to the selection of single-cell clones*

The division of cells supported on a filter paper raft above an actively dividing callus, or at low density in liquid and agar media, all go a long way towards achieving Haberlandt's objective of culturing single vegetative cells of the plant body. Each of these methods is important in its own right, but the plating technique is the one that has the widest application, since it provides a method for the selection of interesting homogeneous single-cell clones from heterogeneous cell suspensions.

In selecting single-cell clones the inoculum must contain as many free cells and as few aggregates as possible. The cells are then plated at, or just above, the minimum effective cell density, so that cell aggregates develop as separate entities. The individual colonies are subsequently transferred to fresh medium when large enough to handle.

An example of the use of the plating technique is provided by the separation of morphologically distinct clones from leaf callus of deadly nightshade. The cultures are normally pale green when grown in the light, but occasionally white areas appear on the tissues, suggesting that the callus is a heterogeneous mass of green and white cells. In a typical experiment, calluses were transferred to liquid medium and the dispersed cells grown for several passages. Free cells and small aggregates from stationary phase

68

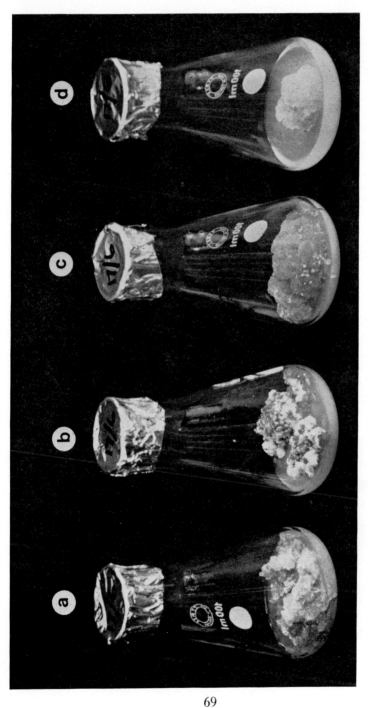

Fig. 4.8. Isolation of clones from *Atropa* leaf callus by Bergmann plates. (*a*) Stock callus from which clones (*b*), (*c*), and (*d*) were isolated. (*b*) Dark green callus growing as hard, irregular masses. (*c*) Crisp, friable light green callus. (*d*) White callus with a soft, wet texture.

69

suspensions were plated in synthetic medium at densities from $1.0–2.0 \times 10^4$ cells per cm^3. Plates were incubated in the dark for three weeks. 2000 individual colonies were then transferred to fresh medium and cultured under a fluorescent lamp. As the colonies grew and developed chloroplast pigments, three distinct clones were selected on their morphology and pigmentation (fig. 4.8). These three clones were retained for further comparative studies, and were found to differ in content of chloroplast pigments, cellular ultrastructure, growth rate, and nutritional requirements when cultured in suspension.

A visual selection system such as the one described above may be used for separating pigmented cell strains, but is inadequate for selecting biochemical or genetical variants from a population in which all the cells are morphologically identical. More powerful selection methods, such as those based on the selection of auxotrophic mutants (cell lines which require a specific metabolite for growth) in different media must be developed before the plating technique can be utilized to its full advantage.

4.6.4. *Reduction of the minimum effective cell density on agar plates*

The methods used to reduce the minimum effective cell density in suspension culture apply equally well in attempting to grow cells on agar plates. Thus, pieces of actively growing nurse callus placed on the surface of the agar will stimulate colony production from plated cells (fig. 4.9), and in sycamore, nurse callus promotes colony formation at plating densities down to 4.0×10^3 cells per cm^3. The

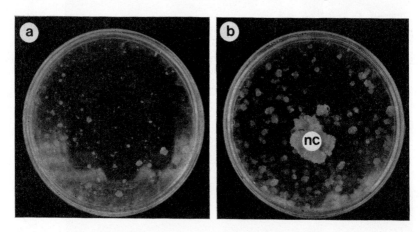

Fig. 4.9. Stimulation of colony production from plated cells of *Atropa* by nurse tissue of the same clone. (*a*) Control. (*b*) Plate with nurse callus (nc).

70

nurse callus can be prevented from over-growing the agar by confining it within a glass ring, the bottom of the ring having holes to permit outwards diffusion of growth promoting compounds into the surrounding medium. Alternatively, a high density nurse suspension can be plated in the bottom of the petri dish, and then covered with a filter paper. The low density test suspension is then spread over the surface of the filter. It is interesting to note that developing cell colonies can themselves exert a nurse effect on other cells in their immediate vicinity. Colony development often begins in localized areas from which it spreads across the plate. Conditioned medium has been incorporated into agar plating medium to reduce the minimum effective cell density, while attempts to alter the gas phase above the agar by incubating inoculated plates in specially constructed boxes fitted with gas inlet and outlet ports have met with some success.

4.6.5. *Methods in use to increase the proportion of free cells in suspensions used as plating inocula*

Several workers have described the isolation of clones that differ in morphology, pigmentation, friability, hormone requirements, and growth rate when they are subjected to the Bergmann plating method. These clones are assumed to have arisen from single cells. However, these results must be viewed with caution, since suspension cultures have a distinct limitation as a starting material for clonal work, which relates to the difficulty of obtaining a cell inoculum consisting entirely of free cells. It may be argued that small cell aggregates are equivalent to single cells, since all the cells within the aggregate will have originated from the same mother cell. This may be true for small aggregates of two or four cells, but it is possible that larger aggregates may be mixtures of cells which will develop into heterogeneous cell colonies. Attempts have therefore been made to increase the proportion of free cells in suspensions by two methods:

4.6.5.1. *Filtration*

The cell suspension is washed through a series of nylon or stainless steel meshes of decreasing pore size which remove the large cell aggregates. The filtrate of single cells and small clumps is then used as plating inocula.

4.6.5.2. *Enzymatic separation of cultured cells*

Two groups of enzymes, the pectinases and cellulases, attack plant cell walls. Pectinases digest the middle lamella causing the cells to separate, while cellulases digest the cellulose structure. These enzymes are discussed in detail in Chapter 5 in connection with

71

protoplast isolation. Theoretically, it should be possible to increase cell dispersion by pectinase alone, although in practice a mixture of both enzymes is usually necessary. The most suitable enzyme concentrations for separating cells without impairing their viability must be determined for the culture under investigation. Since the walls of separated cells are thinner than normal as a result of partial digestion when cellulase is included in the enzyme mixture, the cells must be protected from bursting by including an osmotic stabilizer such as mannitol or sorbitol (used at about 8 per cent w/v) in the medium. Published results for sycamore cultures show that cell separation is increased when low concentrations of enzymes, e.g. 0·5 per cent w/v macerozyme (pectinase) and 0·1 per cent w/v cellulase, are included in the culture medium during a three weeks passage in suspension. At early stationary phase the cultures consist of single cells and cell pairs, providing an improved inoculum for plating.

4.6.6. Growth of cells in micro-chambers

The culture work considered so far has been carried out using large volumes of several millilitres of liquid or agar medium in a variety of culture vessels. Free cells have also been grown in small droplets of a few microlitres of culture medium in micro-chambers constructed on glass microscope slides. Micro-chambers readily allow microscopic observation of individual cells over a period of time, and there are reports of the successful development of free cells to large cellular aggregates in this apparatus. However, this technique has generally seen limited application.

4.7. The isolation of single cells directly from whole plants
4.7.1. Methods in use to dissociate plant tissues

The inherent difficulties of obtaining inocula of completely free cells from suspension cultures indicates the need to find alternative sources of single cells for clonal investigations. Emphasis has been directed towards isolating cells from fully differentiated plant organs, and studying their growth in culture. Leaves are frequently used as a source of free cells, the latter being isolated from the mesophyll tissue by two methods:

4.7.1.1. Mechanical isolation

In early attempts to isolate leaf cells, the mesophyll was exposed by tearing the lamina and the cells were collected by gently scraping the green tissue with a scalpel or other sharp instrument. H. W. Kohlenbach (1966) isolated mesophyll cells of *Macleaya cordata* (see Chapter 1, fig. 1.7) by cutting the lamina into thin strips and agitating the strips in liquid medium. Indeed, he accomplished Haberlandt's aim, since he successfully induced these isolated, fully differentiated chloroplast-containing leaf cells to divide in culture.

More recently, workers have demonstrated the ability of mesophyll cells of some plants to withstand the mechanical shearing forces produced during grinding of the tissue with a ground-glass hand homogenizer. When cladodes of asparagus (*Asparagus officinalis*), a monocotyledon, and leaves of peanut (*Arachis hypogaea*) and morning glory (*Ipomea hederifolia*) (dicotyledons) are homogenized, large quantities of separated cells are rapidly obtained. This is by far the simplest method of isolating free cells directly from higher plants, but unfortunately the method is suitable for only a small number of species.

4.7.1.2. Enzymatic isolation

The enzymatic separation of leaf mesophyll cells from expanded tobacco leaves was first reported from Japan by I. Takebe and co-workers during 1968, and has since been extended to several other

Fig. 4.10.   Removal of the lower epidermis of a *Nicotiana tabacum* leaf to expose the mesophyll tissue.

F

species. The lower epidermis of excised leaves is removed by inserting fine jeweller's forceps beneath the junction of a lateral vein with the midrib, and peeling away the epidermis towards the edge of the lamina (fig. 4.10). Areas of exposed mesophyll are cut from the leaf and incubated with gentle shaking in a pectinase solution. The enzyme is decanted at 30 min intervals over a period of about 3·5 h and replaced with an equal volume of fresh solution at each change. The first enzyme change is discarded, as this contains cells damaged during removal of the lower epidermis, but subsequent aliquots of enzyme contain separated viable mesophyll cells. After washing to remove the enzyme, the free cells are transferred to culture media ready for use as inocula in culture experiments.

4.7.2. *The importance of isolating free-cell inocula from whole plants*

The ease with which large populations of free cells can be isolated from leaves makes mesophyll tissue an attractive source of inocula for studies of cellular de-differentiation and for clonal investigations. Mesophyll cells obtained from a limited number of higher plants will divide in culture to form callus. In the case of *Asparagus* and *Nicotiana*, this tissue readily differentiates shoots from which whole plants can be recovered, while in *Macleaya* the callus forms large numbers of embryoids.

Isolated leaf cells are likely to be extremely important in mutagenesis experiments. Thus, if leaves are exposed to mutagenic agents and cells isolated from this material are plated into selective media, that contain, for example, specific anti-metabolites (antibiotics, amino acid analogues, and fungal or bacterial toxins), or media exhibiting specific physical factors such as increased osmotic pressure, it may be possible to select new mutant cell lines having resistance to these conditions. Plant regeneration from mutant clones could provide the plant breeder with new stocks of genetic material. Mutagenesis studies may be facilitated by the use of haploid plants as a source of mesophyll cells, a subject discussed more fully in Chapters 7 and 8.

Plants regenerated from callus tissues sometimes show aberrations such as the sudden appearance of leaf variegation, or changes in flower colour. These may result from changes in the chromosome complement of the cells during culture. It would therefore be advantageous if free cells could be induced to undergo morphogenesis with the direct production of embryoids without an intervening callus phase. It is now possible to induce microspores to develop directly into embryoids in culture, and it seems logical to assume that this developmental pattern will soon be possible with free cells isolated from cell cultures or directly from plant organs.

74

4.8. *Summary*

In this chapter we have seen how the growth requirements of cells become more complex as the number of cells in the inoculum at sub-culture is reduced, and how these requirements can be provided, to some extent, by metabolites released by a high density population of actively growing cells. In clonal studies it is necessary to plate cells at as low a minimum effective cell density as possible, while still maintaining a high plating efficiency. The use of nurse cultures and conditioned media have greatly assisted this aspect of culture work, since they reduce the inoculum density. Cell colonies then develop as discrete units, which increases the possibility of clones being of single-cell origin. Advances in enzyme technology have seen greater emphasis being placed on the isolation of free cells directly from differentiated plant organs, because of the relative ease with which the cells can be separated. Isolated mesophyll cells of some higher plants readily divide in culture to produce callus, from which whole plants can be regenerated in a few species.

The growth of single cells in culture fulfils Haberlandt's conception of one day being able to grow cells isolated from fully differentiated plant organs. In addition, it is now possible to proceed one step further and to remove completely the wall of many plant cells by enzymatic methods so as to produce large, homogeneous populations of separate naked cells or protoplasts. Some protoplasts will regenerate a new cell wall and undergo division to produce callus tissue. Protoplasts are therefore an ideal starting material for the separation of single-cell clones. In addition, they have many more exciting potential uses, all of which will be subsequently discussed.

CHAPTER 5

higher plant protoplasts—their isolation and behaviour

5.1. *Introduction*

IN the preceding chapter we described the methods used to obtain populations of free cells from certain tissues such as leaf mesophyll, but even with the techniques currently available it is difficult to prepare single-cell inocula from the majority of tissues, especially those grown in culture. As a consequence of this, colonies arising on agar plates frequently develop from small groups of two or more cells. The technique of isolating plant protoplasts now to be described overcomes many of the difficulties associated with the preparation of free cells. It enables the walls of plant cells to be removed, releasing the living protoplasts. In this way it is possible to split a tissue into a homogeneous population of free individual units or naked cells.

The technique has considerable potential in botany, since it permits individual protoplasts to be studied in isolation, where they can express their regenerative ability. Indeed, protoplasts of some species will regenerate a new cell wall, and will divide to produce a callus from which plants can be regenerated. In addition, removal of the cell wall exposes the plasmalemma of the living cell, and allows this surface membrane to be studied in response to direct stimulation by physiologically active substances, inert materials, macromolecules and micro-organisms. Under certain conditions isolated protoplasts will adhere together by their surface membranes. This adhesion may be followed by membrane fusion and cytoplasmic coalescence to give a fusion product of two or more protoplasts. There are also reports of the successful regeneration of whole plants from fused protoplasts (see Chapter 8). Such advances in the manipulation of plant cells open up the possibility of using isolated protoplasts to produce somatic hybrids from species which are normally sexually incompatible.

5.2. *The plant cell and its protoplast*

Plant cells possess a rigid cell wall enclosing the living protoplast. The latter consists of the cytoplasm with its included organelles such as the nucleus, plastids, mitochondria, ribosomes, endoplasmic reticulum, and golgi apparatus, and one or more vacuoles. During normal development there is intimate contact between the cell wall

76

and the surface membrane, the plasmalemma, of the protoplast. Although the plasmalemma is involved in cell wall development, it is not firmly attached to the surrounding wall. Physical contact between this membrane and the wall is maintained by turgor pressure of the protoplast acting outwards against the restraining wall. Under conditions of water stress, such as wilting, the plasmalemma contracts away from the wall as the protoplast loses its turgidity, but resumes contact when the turgidity is restored. The plasmodesmata connecting adjacent cells may be severed if very extensive protoplast contraction occurs during conditions of severe water loss. If the cell walls enclosing contracted protoplasts are removed, the individual protoplasts are released into the surrounding plasmolysing medium (*plasmolyticum* or *osmoticum*). Protoplasts have been isolated from primary tissues of most plant organs including roots, leaves, petals, fruits, coleoptiles and storage organs, and from highly specialized structures such as developing pollen grains (microspores) and root nodules of leguminous plants. Callus and suspension cells also yield protoplasts, and because of their sterility are an attractive source of naked cells.

5.3. *The release of protoplasts from cell walls*

5.3.1. *Methods of protoplast release*

5.3.1.1. *Plasmolytica*

Irrespective of their source, isolated protoplasts share a common feature of being osmotically fragile. Consequently, before release from the cell wall they must be stabilized with a solution that is hypertonic but not too hypertonic; if they are not, they expand as the wall pressure is removed and eventually burst. Since they are naked cells, they are unable to withstand the physical shocks to which whole cells may be accustomed, and therefore require gentle handling at all times.

Protoplasts are released from the confines of their surrounding cell walls either mechanically or enzymatically. In both methods the cells are first plasmolysed by solutions of sugars such as mannitol and sorbitol; these are preferred since they are metabolically relatively inert. Other sugars such as glucose and sucrose are absorbed and metabolized, especially during the extended periods sometimes required for enzymatic isolation of protoplasts. This frequently results in protoplast instability during subsequent culture. The solution into which the protoplasts are released is normally hypertonic in relation to the cell sap. The most suitable osmotic pressure of the plasmolyticum must be determined empirically and will vary with the tissue, e.g. protoplasts from leaves of plants such as tobacco and cowpea (*Vigna sinensis*) are normally isolated in 13 per cent w/v (0·7 M) mannitol, whereas those of crown gall callus tissue of Virginia creeper (*Parthenocissus tricuspidata*) are isolated in 11 per cent w/v mannitol. Freshly isolated protoplasts should be gently rounded in shape (with the exception of legume root nodule protoplasts). Under-plasmolysis results in bursting; over-plasmolysis leads to a crenated appearance.

5.3.1.2. *Mechanical isolation*

The plasmolysed tissue is cut with a sharp razor, and the protoplasts are released from the ends of the cut cells. Their release is aided by gently squeezing or manipulating the tissue, or by gradually decreasing the osmotic pressure of the bathing solution so that the protoplasts swell and extrude from the cut cells. J. Klerker in 1892 first reported the release of protoplasts from cells of the water soldier (*Stratiotes aloides*) by this mechanical method. It has since been used to obtain protoplasts from epidermis of onion bud scales, cucumber mesocarp, and storage tissues. However, it has seen limited application, since small yields of protoplasts are obtained. It is suitable only for tissues with large cells in which substantial protoplast contraction occurs during plasmolysis, as this minimises damage to the cell contents during slicing of the tissue.

5.3.1.3. *Enzymatic isolation*

The cell walls are removed by hydrolytic enzymes. The primary walls of higher plant cells are based upon a framework of cellulose (a long chain polymer of β1–4 linked D-glucose molecules). In undifferentiated cells, such as those from the region of elongation of young maize roots, cellulose amounts to about 25 to 40 per cent of the dry weight of the wall material. Other monosaccharides such as mannose, galactose, and xylose undergo polymerization to give mannans, galactans and xylans, which in turn form short-chain hemicelluloses, which may represent about 50 per cent of the wall weight. Also present are lipids (5 to 10 per cent) and protein (about 5 per cent). The relative proportions of wall constituents vary as cells differentiate, and generally the amount of cellulose increases with age. It may constitute up to 94 per cent of the dry weight of the wall material in mature cotton hairs. Hemicellulose, protein and lipid decrease or disappear, but lignin, an aromatic polymer of phenylpropane with *p*-coumarylic acid and sinapylic acid, may increase as cells differentiate. The intercellular layer, the middle lamella, consists mainly of pectic acid, itself composed of long chains of galacturonic acid residues. Pectic acid is present in the form of its calcium and magnesium salts, and is responsible for the adhesion of adjacent cells.

The chemical nature of the constituents of the primary wall and middle lamella makes them susceptible to attack by the enzymes cellulase, hemicellulase and pectinase. However, the variation in the nature of cell walls necessitates the use of different enzyme combinations, concentrations, and times of incubation for every particular tissue. Leaf tissues, for example, generally require treatment with cellulase and pectinase to release protoplasts. In some fruits natural hydrolysis of the middle lamella during ripening releases free cells from which protoplasts can be isolated by cellulase. Conversely, fruits with a high pectin content will release protoplasts when treated with pectinase. Some cell walls are easily removed by hydrolytic enzymes; others may be completely resistant to enzymic degradation.

Most of the cell wall degrading enzymes used for isolating protoplasts come from fungi. Indeed, the release of protoplasts from root tips of tomato by E. C. Cocking in 1960 using cellulase produced by precipitation of the protein fraction from culture filtrates of the mould *Myrothecium verrucaria*, was the first report of the successful enzymatic isolation of higher plant protoplasts. Fungal cellulases are now commercially available under various trade names, such as ' Cellulase Onozuka ', ' Meicelase P ', and ' Driselase '. ' Rhozyme ' shows hemicellulase as well as cellulase activity. Cellulases have important application in the food industry for softening and homogenizing plant tissues, in brewing, and in the production of animal feeding stuffs. The recent realization of their importance in botanical research has been followed by a substantial increase in their price.

The preparation of cellulases is a simple industrial process. Aerated wheat bran cultures of *Trichoderma viride* are harvested after three days growth at 25°C. The cultures are pressed, washed, and filtered and cellulase released into the culture medium during fungal growth is precipitated with ammonium sulphate. The enzyme is de-salted, concentrated, and spray-dried to give a light brown powder. As a result of this simple precipitation procedure some commercial cellulases are impure mixtures containing other enzymes such as cellobiose, gluconase, xylanase, lipase, phospholipase, nucleases, chitinase, $\beta 1-3$ glucanase (both the latter acting on fungal cell walls), and a certain degree of pectinase activity.

Pectinases are produced by *Rhizopus* species, and some are also sold under trade names such as ' Macerozyme ' and ' Pectinol R10 '. Although most cell-wall degrading enzymes come from fungi, the gastric juice obtained by squeezing out the mid-intestinal gland secretion from the gut of freshly killed, starved Roman snails (*Helix pomatia*) is frequently used for digesting cell walls. Some protoplast laboratories breed their own snails. Snail enzyme is available commercially as a liquid ' Glusulase ', as ' Suc digestif de *Helix pomatia* ', and as a powder ' Helicase '.

79

Increase in the specific activity and purity of commercial enzymes may be necessary to effect protoplast release from some tissues. This can be achieved by removal of low molecular weight impurities from the enzymes by ion-exchange resins. The purified enzymes are then freeze dried. Enzyme purity may be important for subsequent viability of released protoplasts, but in some instances protoplast release actually declines with increase in enzyme purity. The complexity of the impurities present in wall-degrading enzymes which can act on the cytoplasm during incubation, demands that the cells are immersed in the enzymes for the minimum period of time necessary to effect wall degradation.

5.3.2. The enzymatic isolation of protoplasts from leaves and cultured cells

Protoplasts are isolated enzymatically by procedures employing a sequential method or a mixed enzyme treatment. These methods will be illustrated by reference to the isolation of protoplasts from leaves and cultured cells, since protoplasts from these sources have probably been used in more investigations than those from other sources. Leaf material requires surface sterilization by conventional procedures described in Chapter 2. Enzyme solutions are thermolabile and must be filter sterilized.

5.3.2.1. Sequential method

This is a two-step procedure. Cells are separated enzymatically by shaking peeled leaf tissue, for example of tobacco, in pectinase or mechanically by grinding tissue, for example of asparagus, in a hand homogenizer. These methods of separating mesophyll cells have already been described in Chapter 4. The free cells are then incubated in cellulase to remove their cell walls.

The buoyancy of isolated protoplasts allows them to be washed free of enzyme and debris. Released protoplasts sink when mannitol or sorbitol are used as plasmolytica; the digested material is collected as a pellet by gentle centrifugation, and the enzyme supernatant containing fine debris is discarded. Pelleted protoplasts are resuspended in a washing solution containing sucrose as plasmolyticum; when gently centrifuged the protoplasts now rise to the surface and float just below the meniscus, while debris and undigested cells sediment. The protoplasts are removed with a pasteur pipette, and washed by resuspension and gentle centrifugation in mannitol or sucrose solutions. They are then ready for experimental purposes.

The sequential enzyme method works well for mesophyll tissue of some leaves such as those of tobacco, but in other cases shaking of the leaf pieces during pectinase treatment causes the protoplasts to burst within their cell walls. A modification of the technique has been used to overcome this bursting problem. The peeled leaves are incubated statically with their exposed mesophyll in contact with the surface of the pectinase, followed by static incubation in cellulase. Protoplasts are then released by gentle agitation. Penetration of enzymes is facilitated by vacuum infiltration, but protoplast yields are generally lower than when the leaf tissue is first shaken in pectinase to release free cells.

5.3.2.2. Mixed-enzyme treatment

This is a single-step procedure employing a mixture of cellulase and pectinase; cell separation and wall degradation occur simultaneously. The peeled leaf tissue is incubated statically, with the exposed mesophyll in contact with the surface of the enzyme solution. Released protoplasts are cleaned by the washing procedures already described.

So far we have considered the release of mesophyll protoplasts. The upper and lower epidermis of some leaves, e.g. those of tobacco, also yield viable protoplasts during enzyme treatment with a mixture of cellulase and pectinase. If digestion of the leaf tissue proceeds to completion, the upper epidermal protoplasts are released with those from the mesophyll. However, the two types can be separated by their buoyancy. When centrifuged in mannitol or sorbitol, the epidermal protoplasts form a pale yellowish-green coloured band just below the liquid meniscus, while the bright green mesophyll protoplasts sediment. During the initial peeling of the leaf to expose the mesophyll, the lower epidermis is normally discarded after removal from the lamina. However, this also releases protoplasts when incubated, cuticle uppermost, on the surface of enzyme mixture. All that remain on the enzyme after digestion are the leaf cuticle and guard cells. The walls of the latter are resistant to enzyme attack.

Most reports of the isolation of protoplasts from cultured cells have employed a mixed-enzyme treatment. Exposure of the cells to the enzymes merely necessitates their transfer into the enzyme solution, which reduces the manipulative stages and decreases the chances of contamination. A friable tissue is clearly advantageous in facilitating penetration of enzymes to their site of activity. Cells of cultured tissues such as carrot and soybean, and certain cell lines of crown gall origin, e.g. those of carrot and Virginia creeper, readily yield protoplasts in large numbers. However, cultured cells and whole plant tissues all present special technical problems, each of which must be solved for the tissue under investigation.

81

5.3.3. General problems associated with the isolation of protoplasts from whole plant tissues and cultured cells

Difficulties are frequently experienced in preparing whole plant tissues for enzyme incubation. The lower epidermis of leaves of some dicotyledonous genera such as *Nicotiana* and *Vigna* is easily removed with fine forceps. In contrast, leaves of monocotyledons are particularly difficult to peel, and the leaf material is generally cut into narrow longitudinal strips before immersion in enzyme. Some workers include a cuticle-degrading enzyme in their cell-wall digestion mixture to overcome the need to remove the epidermis.

The enzyme concentrations required to release protoplasts vary according to the growth characteristics of the tissue. In cultured cells, the ease with which the walls can be removed even from tissue isolates of the same species is often strain-dependent, and may differ between cells originally derived from the same clone but cultured under different physical conditions in different laboratories. Furthermore, the degradation of cell walls is often critically dependent upon the age following sub-culture of the callus or suspension to fresh medium, and the overall period of time that the cells have been in culture. Generally protoplasts are easier to prepare from actively growing cells.

Only rarely do cultured cells give complete liberation of protoplasts when treated with wall degrading enzymes. Protoplasts released from some cell cultures are easily separated from undigested material by centrifugation procedures similar to those already described for mesophyll protoplasts. In other cases the separation of released protoplasts from undigested cells presents a major problem, as both may have similar buoyancy and remain mixed together whatever plasmolyticum is employed in the washing procedure. Washing of the digested material on a nylon or stainless steel filter of a suitable pore size to permit passage of released protoplasts but not of undigested cells, has been used with varying degrees of success to separate protoplasts and cells. It is often not possible to guarantee a homogeneous preparation of protoplasts uncontaminated by cells, and such preparations have disadvantages for critical work. Some tissues are resistant to enzyme degradation, and although cell cultures are potentially a very useful source of protoplasts, this material frequently has distinct limitations.

5.4. Properties of isolated protoplasts

5.4.1. Morphology

The enzymatic release of protoplasts from free cells can be followed microscopically by observing the disappearance of the wall and subsequent rounding of the protoplasts. The size and appearance of released protoplasts are related to the nature of the parent cells. Protoplasts from similar tissues are morphologically comparable whether isolated from dicotyledons or monocotyledons. Green leaf mesophyll protoplasts normally have a large central vacuole with the chloroplasts evenly distributed around the periphery of the cytoplasm (fig. 5.1 *a, b*). Leaf epidermal protoplasts are easily distinguished from those of the mesophyll by their pale yellowish-green colour, fewer plastids and prominent cytoplasmic strands (fig. 5.1 *c, d*). Petal protoplasts may be coloured by pigments within their vacuoles. Cultured cells normally yield creamy-coloured protoplasts, and if starch is present their plastids are highly refractive (fig. 5.1 *e*). Protoplasts of vacuolated cells are generally about 25 to 60 μm in diameter. Those of meristematic cells, pollen mother cells and pollen tetrads (fig. 5.1 *f, g*) are smaller, about 12 to 20 μm in size. Conversely, protoplasts from the infected tissue of legume root nodules may be over 200 μm in size. Unlike other protoplasts they generally remain elongate after cell wall removal, since their shape is determined by the overall number and distribution of bacteroids in their cytoplasm (fig. 5.1 *h, i*).

5.4.2. *Osmotic characteristics of isolated protoplasts*

Isolated protoplasts quickly respond to changes in osmotic pressure of the bathing medium. If this is rapidly decreased, the protoplasts expand, the plasmalemma ruptures, and the protoplasts collapse. Bursting is frequently accompanied by expulsion of vacuoles and chloroplasts. Increasing the osmotic pressure of the plasmoly-ticum causes protoplasts to contract. This can equally well result in damage, by its effect on dehydration and metabolism, and by physical damage resulting from the larger organelles such as chloroplasts protruding through the plasmalemma. Protoplasts can withstand changing pressures so long as they are gradual and within a small range either side of the plasmolyticum level employed for isolation.

5.4.3. *Uptake phenomena*

The plasmalemma of isolated plant protoplasts should be thought of not as a tightly stretched surface, as in the case of an inflated balloon, but as a structure capable of altering its shape by developing outgrowths as well as invaginations. Extensive ultrastructural studies on isolated protoplasts have demonstrated the frequent occurrence of vesicles within their cytoplasm. Each vesicle is surrounded by a single membrane, which in many cases originates as an invagination of the plasmalemma into the cytoplasm. The open

83

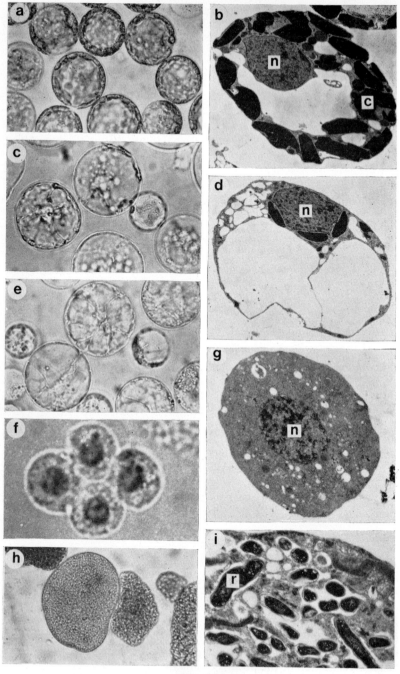

Fig. 5.1.

84

end of the invagination then seals by membrane fusion, to release the vesicle into the cytoplasm.

Vesicles are thought to be of two types:

5.4.3.1. *Plasmolytic vesicles*

These are often several μm across and originate as gross infoldings of the plasmalemma into the cytoplasm as the protoplast contracts during plasmolysis. Some of these plasmolytic vesicles are large enough to accommodate micro-organisms. Indeed, if the soil bacterium *Rhizobium japonicum* normally responsible for fixing atmospheric nitrogen in root nodules of cowpea is grown in culture, and large numbers of bacteria are included in the enzyme mixture during the isolation of mesophyll protoplasts from cowpea leaves, bacterial cells may be found within vesicles in the cytoplasm of some of the isolated protoplasts (fig. 5.2 *a*, *b*). The cell walls of the bacteria

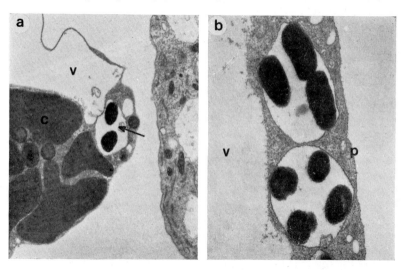

Fig. 5.2. Electron micrographs of isolated mesophyll protoplasts of *Vigna sinensis*, showing: (*a*) Uptake of two *Rhizobium* cells (arrowed) into a vesicle in the cytoplasm (× 8000). (*b*) Membrane-bounded vesicles enclosing bacteria (× 14 000). c = chloroplast; p = plasmalemma; v = vacuole.

Fig. 5.1. Light and electron micrographs of protoplasts freshly isoated from: (*a*), (*b*) *Nicotiana tabacum* leaf mesophyll tissue (× 450, × 2500). (*c*), (*d*) Epidermis of *Nicotiana tabacum* leaves (× 450, × 2500). (*e*) Cultured cells of *Daucus carota* (× 450). (*f*), (*g*) Pollen tetrads of *Nicotiana tabacum* (× 1650, × 7500). (*h*), (*i*) Infected tissue of root nodules of *Glycine max*. (× 220, × 9000). r = *Rhizobium* bacteroid; c = chloroplast; n = nucleus.

are resistant to degradation by the hydrolytic enzymes which digest the walls of the higher plant cells. As the bacteria are included in the enzyme mixture, they are able to penetrate to the plasmalemma immediately the plant cell wall is weakened by the enzymes. Bacteria arriving at the surface of a protoplast while the plasmalemma is still infolding during plasmolysis may be taken up into invaginations and eventually come to lie in membrane-bounded vesicles in the cytoplasm. The uptake of bacteria is probably assisted by their motility.

5.4.3.2. *Pinocytotic vesicles*

These are smaller than plasmolytic vesicles and arise both during removal of the wall and following isolation of the protoplast. In animal cells, pinocytosis is defined as the entry of material into cells via invaginations of the plasmalemma. The extent to which this normally occurs in intact plant cells is uncertain, and the direct evidence for this phenomenon in plants has come mainly from studies with protoplasts. Removal of the cell wall appears to stimulate activity of the surface membrane. The extent of pinocytosis depends upon the protoplast system being studied, and upon the constituents of the plasmolyticum. As pinocytosis generally involves an initial adsorption on to the plasmalemma of the material to be taken up, the surface charge of this material in relation to the charge of the plasmalemma is critical. Polycations such as poly-L-ornithine can alter the charge on the plasmalemma, and are sometimes used at very low concentration (1 to 2 μg per cm^3) to stimulate uptake.

In order to demonstrate pinocytosis, the freshly isolated protoplasts are incubated in a suitable plasmolyticum containing the material to be taken up, for a period of a few minutes to several hours. Uptake of inert materials, such as small polystyrene latex spheres about 0·3 μm in diameter, and particles of thorium dioxide (fig. 5.3 *a*, *b*), and organic macromolecules, e.g. ferritin (fig. 5.3 *c*) and viruses, into pinocytotic vesicles in protoplasts has been shown by electron microscopy.

The two mechanisms described both involve uptake of particulate materials or micro-organisms into cytoplasmic vesicles. Radioactive labelling experiments have demonstrated uptake of macromolecules such as nucleic acids, e.g. bacterial DNA from *Escherichia coli* and RNA from Tobacco Mosaic Virus (TMV), into higher plant protoplasts. However, it is not known whether these macromolecules pass directly through the plasmalemma, or whether they first enter pinocytotic vesicles and are later released into the cytoplasm. There have also been reports of the uptake of isolated nuclei and chloroplasts into higher plant protoplasts, but again the mechanism of uptake is not clear.

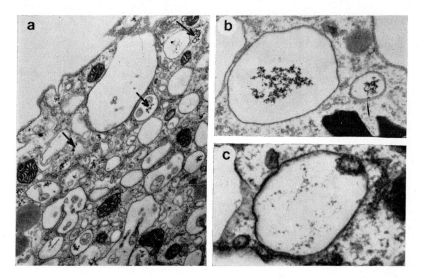

Fig. 5.3. Electron micrographs illustrating pinocytotic uptake of particles by isolated mesophyll protoplasts of *Nicotiana tabacum*. (*a*) Uptake of thorium dioxide (arrowed) into membrane-bounded vesicles in the cytoplasm (×14 000). (*b*) Higher magnification of vesicles containing thorium dioxide (×28 000). (*c*) Ferritin molecules in a pinocytotic vesicle (×32 000).

5.4.4. *Protoplast fusion*

Under certain conditions protoplasts may come together, and their surface membranes and cytoplasms may coalesce to form large protoplasts (fusion bodies) containing two or more nuclei. Protoplast fusion is of two types, induced and spontaneous.

5.4.4.1. *Induced fusion*

Certain conditions provided in the plasmolyticum will induce freely dispersed, individual protoplasts to adhere by their surface membranes; such as a suitable ionic environment provided by a sodium salt solution, particularly sodium nitrate. Subjecting protoplasts to high alkalinity in a buffer of glycine and sodium hydroxide containing calcium to stabilize the plasmalemma, or treating with polyethylene glycol solution are other ways of stimulating protoplast adhesion (fig. 5.4 *a*, *b*). Plasmalemma adhesion may be followed by membrane fusion in the regions of contact, which establishes continuity between the cytoplasms of the protoplasts. This is usually followed by rounding of the fusion product (fig. 5.4 *c*). Whether or not the process proceeds as far as cytoplasmic coalescence depends on the extent of contact of the surface membranes and the time for which this contact is maintained. Protoplast size, the degree of vacuolation, and the distribution of larger organelles, are also important. Meristematic protoplasts fuse more readily than vacuolated ones; peripheral chloroplasts in vacuolated leaf protoplasts inhibit fusion.

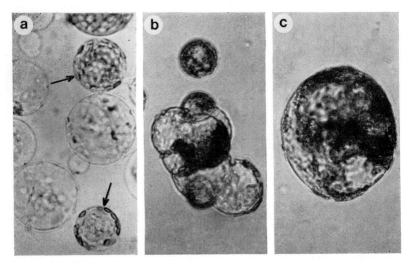

Fig. 5.4. Polyethylene glycol-induced fusion of green mesophyll protoplasts of *Vigna sinensis* with yellowish-green leaf epidermal protoplasts of *Nicotiana tabacum*. (*a*) Mixture of mesophyll (arrowed) and epidermal protoplasts before fusion treatment. (*b*) Aggregate of adhering protoplasts after fusion treatment. (*c*) A large rounded fusion body (× 500).

Although induced fusion is a controlled event requiring the protoplasts to be treated with an inducing agent, the initial adhesion is a random process and may involve two or more protoplasts. When more than two protoplasts fuse, multinucleate bodies result. In any treatment some protoplasts will remain single and unfused. Fusion is not restricted to protoplasts isolated from the same tissue; leaf protoplasts will fuse with callus protoplasts from the same or different genera or species. The fusion bodies resulting from the induced fusion of protoplasts whose nuclei have identical genotypes are homokaryons, while fusion of protoplasts with different genotypes gives heterokaryons. The latter are biologically more meaningful than homokaryons, since they form the basic step of somatic hybridization, a technique which provides a potential means of crossing plants which are normally sexually incompatible.

88

Induced fusion of protoplasts of different genera or species does not result solely in heterokaryon formation. As adhesion is a random process, both heterokaryons and homokaryons occur amongst the fusion products, and methods therefore have to be devised to select the interesting material for subsequent study. This may sometimes be done by sight after fusion; if the protoplasts from the two plants that are to be crossed are morphologically different, e.g. green mesophyll protoplasts and pale yellowish-green leaf epidermal protoplasts (fig. 5.4 a), heterokaryons with morphological characteristics of the two types can be distinguished (fig. 5.4 c). Alternatively, interesting heterokaryons may be encouraged to develop by culturing the protoplasts in media that selectively promote development of heterokaryons, but not of homokaryons or unfused protoplasts.

5.4.4.2. *Spontaneous fusion*

Plasmolysis during enzyme treatment usually severs the plasmodesmata connecting adjacent cells, but occasionally they remain unbroken. During degradation of walls the areas of them between the plasmodesmata are digested, allowing the plasmodesmata to expand, and permitting free passage of cytoplasm and organelles between adjacent protoplasts. The fusion of adjacent protoplasts during wall degradation requires no inducing agent and is termed spontaneous fusion.

Some degree of spontaneous fusion, perhaps only at very low frequency (usually less than 0·1 per cent of the total population), occurs in protoplasts isolated from cultured cells. Its incidence varies in protoplasts isolated from whole plant tissues. The presence of spontaneous fusion bodies in preparations of leaf mesophyll protoplasts is frequently related to the cultural conditions of the plants, especially if they receive seasonal variation in temperature and light intensity under greenhouse conditions.

Biological membranes will sometimes fuse of their own accord. This normally occurs during fertilization, when the pollen tube fuses with the embryo sac. The plasmalemmata of freshly isolated protoplasts are in frequent contact, and have the opportunity to adhere and fuse; such fusion may be classed as another form of spontaneous fusion. Thus, the term usually refers to protoplast fusion during wall degradation, but it may equally well be applied to coalescence of protoplasts after isolation in the absence of a fusion agent.

5.5. *The culture of higher plant protoplasts*
5.5.1. *Introduction*

The earlier attempts to culture protoplasts employed liquid media, but during 1970 a significant advance was made by I. Takebe,

G. Labib and G. Melchers who successfully plated isolated protoplasts of tobacco leaf mesophyll in medium made semi-solid with 0·6 per cent agar. Their method is now routinely used for culturing protoplasts from a variety of tissues.

Dispersing isolated protoplasts in agar medium is a simple procedure. The naked cells are first suspended in liquid culture medium at a density equal to twice the final plating density. The protoplast suspension is then transferred to a petri plate, and an equal volume of culture medium with 1·2 per cent w/v agar at 40°C is quickly but gently added to the protoplast suspension. The whole is swirled to disperse the protoplasts throughout the medium, and then left undisturbed until the agar has set. The incubation conditions for protoplasts are similar to those for cell cultures. Some grow well in the dark, others, particularly those from leaves, are best maintained under low intensity light. Over-illumination results in bleaching of chlorophyll and protoplast collapse.

The media for protoplasts must contain a plasmolyticum, generally mannitol. Other media constituents are similar to those used for cell cultures. Protoplasts are cultured in media only a few millimetres in depth, so that aeration is not inhibited. Those in liquid culture are incubated statically in suitable vessels, e.g. petri dishes, small flasks, screw-capped tubes and micro-chambers, but if wall regeneration occurs they can be gently shaken and eventually treated as a cell suspension.

5.5.2. Cell wall regeneration by cultured protoplasts

The ability of higher plant protoplasts to regenerate a new cell wall was known as long ago as 1897, when C. O. Townsend reported that plasmolysed protoplasts of intact cells of Canadian pondweed (*Elodea canadensis*) and blanket flower (*Gaillardia lanceolata*) would regenerate a new wall *within* the original cell wall. Wall formation was correlated with the presence of a nucleus in the cytoplasm.

The regenerative capacity of isolated protoplasts varies. Some survive only a few hours after isolation, while others live for several days or weeks before collapsing. Conversely, those of some plants are stimulated into intense metabolic activity on isolation. They synthesize a new cell wall, and the regenerated cells may subsequently divide to form cell colonies.

The very early events of the formation of a new wall must be studied with the electron microscope. They may begin within a few hours of transfer of the isolated protoplast to culture medium, as was first reported for isolated tomato fruit locule protoplasts by E. C. Cocking and his colleagues. However, regeneration in the tomato fruit system is atypical, as the wall develops a multilamellar component prior to synthesis of the cellulose layer. More recent studies on wall regeneration by leaf and cultured cell protoplasts have shown the new wall to be similar in appearance in thin section to primary cell walls in the intact tissue. Synthetic activity results in the development of a fine web of cellulose fibrils over the originally naked plasmalemma (fig. 5.5 a, b) by about the third day of culture. Vesicles, probably containing cell wall material, are sometimes pinched off from the surface membrane (fig. 5.5 b); they may contain electron-opaque material originating in the cytoplasm. They become entrapped amongst the fibrils (fig. 5.5 c), and later disappear, presumably as their contents become incorporated into the developing wall. After about 5 to 10 days of culture the fibrils are densely interwoven and the new wall appears similar in section to the walls of cultured cells (fig. 5.5 d). Sometimes wall formation is incomplete. This results

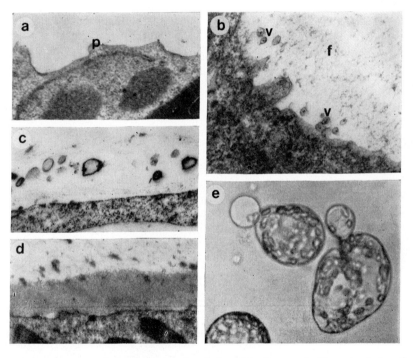

Fig. 5.5. Cell wall regeneration by isolated leaf mesophyll protoplasts of *Vigna sinensis* in culture. (a) The naked plasmalemma (p) of a freshly isolated protoplast (× 23 000). (b) Cellulose fibrils (f) over the plasmalemma after three days in culture. Vesicles (v) are being pinched off from the surface membrane (× 34 000). (c) Vesicles entrapped amongst fibrils of the new wall (× 24 500). (d) Regenerated wall after 10 days in culture (× 20 000). (e) 'Budding' protoplasts (× 260).

in protoplast 'budding' regions of the cytoplasm protruding through weaknesses in the cell wall (fig. 5.5 e), since the latter is unable to resist the outward forces produced by changes in the shape and position of internal vacuoles. Wall regeneration by closely adpressed protoplasts produces a common wall between the adjacent plasmalemmata. In the light microscope the protoplasts are seen to change their shape as a result of mutual pressure, and usually adhere together to form a tissue-like mass.

5.5.3. *Other morphological and structural changes occurring during early culture*

Protoplasts normally expand during the early stages of wall regeneration and assume an oval shape (fig. 5.6 a). Increase in the amount of cytoplasm is accompanied by active cyclosis. Plastids and mitochondria multiply and aggregate in the cytoplasm around the nucleus. The latter often moves to a central position in the regenerating cell (fig. 5.6 b; cf. appearance of freshly isolated protoplasts in section, fig. 5.1 b). There is also an increase in ribosomes, particularly as polysome groups, and of endoplasmic reticulum membranes, which are predominantly rough at this stage. Grana in chloroplasts gradually disappear as these organelles de-differentiate into starch-storing amyloplasts typical of cultured cells. This change occurs in protoplasts cultured in darkness and in the light.

5.5.4. *Cell colony formation*

Wall regeneration is not necessarily followed by cell division. In culture this demands the synthesis of new cytoplasm, and if intense metabolic activity is not resumed the regenerated cells fail to divide. A medium which supports wall regeneration may be unsuitable for inducing division and sustained growth of cells regenerated from protoplasts. Similarly, a medium containing growth hormones suitable for division of regenerated cells may be unsuitable for inducing wall regeneration as the hormones may act directly on the naked plasmalemma, causing expansion with eventual bursting

---

Fig. 5.6. Cell division and colony formation by isolated mesophyll protoplasts of *Vigna sinensis*. (a) Expanding protoplasts after three days in culture (× 300). (b) Thin section of an expanding protoplast. Organelles are clustered around the nucleus (n). p = plastid; v = vacuole (× 1600). (c) The first division in protoplasts (arrowed). The upper protoplast has formed a pair of daughter cells. In the lower protoplasts the division wall is developing from one side (× 300). (d) Thin section through a pair of daughter cells (× 1200). (e) Development of the new cell plate (arrowed) from one side of the regenerated parent cell. n = daughter nuclei (× 1900). (f) A small cell colony (× 300). (g) Cell colonies growing on an agar plate (× 1).

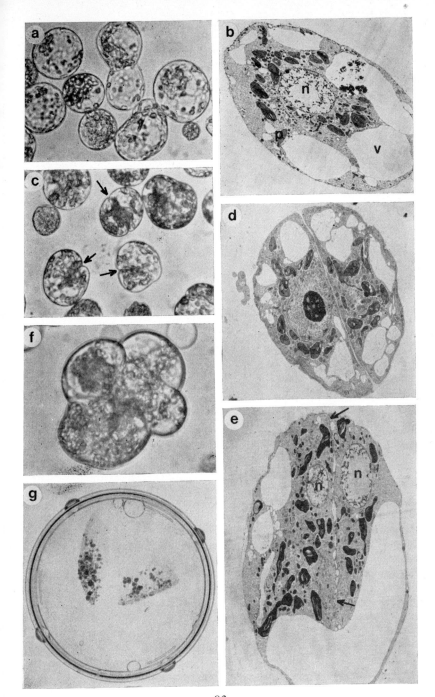

93

and collapse of the isolated protoplasts. Hence, it may be necessary to culture the protoplasts in a medium which initially induces wall regeneration, and then to transfer the regenerated cells to a medium promoting division. Conversely, some isolated protoplasts will regenerate a new wall and subsequently divide in the same medium.

The first division produces two daughter cells, usually of equal size in a dumb-bell-like configuration (fig. 5.6 c, d). At cytokinesis the new cell plate frequently grows across the cytoplasm between the two daughter nuclei from one side of the regenerated parent cell (fig. 5.6 c, e). In this way the first division wall is able to cross any large vacuoles in a tongue-like ingrowth of cytoplasm. This pattern of cytokinesis has already been discussed in considering the fine structure of cultured cells (Chapter 4), and is important in regenerating protoplasts as it permits highly vacuolated cells to divide. Subsequent divisions produce cell colonies (fig. 5.6 f), which become visible to the naked eye (fig. 5.6 g). Cells regenerated from green protoplasts are normally creamy-brown in colour after about three weeks growth when cultured in the light. They may slowly re-green as chloroplasts re-differentiate, but even in green cells the internal membrane system of the plastids never reaches the same level of complexity as the granal membranes in chloroplasts of leaf cells.

A gradual reduction of the osmotic pressure of the culture medium (de-plasmolysis) is necessary to maintain a maximal rate of division, otherwise protoplasts of the regenerated cells undergo secondary plasmolysis and contract away from their regenerated walls. De-plasmolysis in liquid medium is easily achieved by gradually diluting the plasmolyticum. In agar culture, blocks of medium containing dividing protoplasts are transferred to the surface of fresh medium of the same nutrient composition but with reduced plasmolyticum. When cell colonies appear above the agar surface they are maintained as normal calluses by regular transfer. Cells regenerated in liquid media are treated in the way already described for suspension cells. Eventually, the cells regenerated from protoplasts are maintained in medium without plasmolyticum.

In culturing isolated protoplasts it is important to obtain an estimate of the number of them in a population that are capable of forming cell colonies. This is known as the plating efficiency, and is defined as the percentage of protoplasts originally transferred to culture which develop into visible colonies. In tobacco leaf protoplasts the plating efficiency may be as high as 60 per cent, but in other systems it is more frequently less than 5 per cent.

In order to obtain a growth response, protoplasts of most species must be plated at high density, usually above 10^4 protoplasts per cm^3 As we have already seen in Chapter 4, high density inocula are unsuitable for investigations aimed at isolating single-cell clones, since

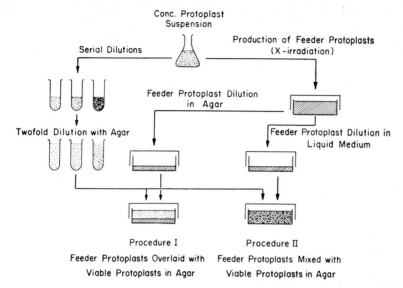

Fig. 5.7. The technique of using X-irradiated protoplasts as feeder cells to stimulate growth of viable protoplasts at low plating density.

adjacent colonies coalesce at an early stage in their development. However, the minimum effective density of protoplasts in agar can be reduced by employing conditioned media and nurse tissue. A novel way of using nurse cells to promote division of protoplasts at low density is provided by the technique of D. Raveh, E. Huberman and E. Galun. They found that X-irradiated protoplasts failed to divide in agar medium, but would act as feeder (nurse) cells and promote growth of viable protoplasts. The feeder protoplasts were either layered beneath, or mixed with, the viable protoplasts in agar (fig. 5.7). In some of their experiments, irradiated diploid tobacco mesophyll protoplasts were used as a high density feeder layer beneath viable diploid or haploid mesophyll protoplasts. These feeder protoplasts promoted colony formation by the diploid protoplasts at plating densities down to 10^3 protoplasts per cm^3, while the inoculum density of the haploid protoplasts was further reduced to 10^2 protoplasts per cm^3 by this technique (fig. 5.8).

5.5.5. *Regeneration of whole plants from protoplasts*
Only a few protoplast-derived calluses will regenerate shoots capable of being grown to flowering plants. At present, these are limited to calluses from leaf mesophyll protoplasts of tobacco, *Petunia*, and rape (*Brassica napus*), from leaf epidermal protoplasts of tobacco, from

95

protoplasts of cladodes of asparagus (a monocotyledon), and from protoplasts of cultured carrot cells. Calluses regenerated from protoplasts are transferred to suitable media to induce morphogenesis. Regenerated shoots are stimulated to develop adventitious roots, transferred to potting compost, and grown to flowering. In tobacco, the period of time from protoplast isolation to flowering is about 100 to 120 days. Since a callus tissue derived from one protoplast may be induced to form several shoots, a stand of plants can readily be obtained from a single naked cell.

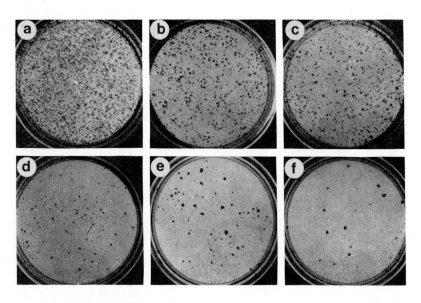

Fig. 5.8. *Nicotiana tabacum;* stimulation of colony formation at low density from haploid mesophyll protoplasts by feeder protoplasts. (*a*) Control —protoplasts plated at high density (5×10^4 protoplasts per cm³) without feeder protoplasts. (*b*), (*c*), (*d*), (*e*) and (*f*). Protoplasts plated at 10^4, 5×10^3, 10^3, 5×10^2 and 10^2 protoplasts per cm³ respectively, over a feeder layer containing 3×10^4 X-irradiated protoplasts per cm³.

5.6. *Summary*

Advances in our knowledge of cell wall chemistry and enzyme technology have resulted in the development of procedures for the enzymatic isolation of higher plant protoplasts in large numbers. Enzymatic digestion reduces many primary tissues to an homogeneous population of separate, individual units. The isolation of naked cells, often by a single-step enzyme treatment, overcomes many of the problems normally encountered in attempting to obtain free-cell inocula for clonal investigations.

Major advances have been made in the handling and culture of osmotically fragile protoplasts since the late 1960s, opening up exciting fields of study of great potential. The ability of isolated protoplasts to take up macromolecules, particulate materials, and micro-organisms, enables them to be used as an experimental system for attempting to modify existing plant cells by the introduction of foreign materials or new genetic information. Furthermore, fusion of somatic cell protoplasts may enable crosses to be obtained between plant species which are normally sexually incompatible. Such experimental approaches may provide the plant breeder with new and valuable stocks of genetic material.

CHAPTER 6
morphogenesis in cell cultures

6.1. *Introduction*

HABERLANDT'S remarkable prophecy that one should be able to make ' artificial embryos ' from free-living angiosperm cells has been recently verified for some plant species. Under certain conditions calluses and cell suspensions obtained either from complex explants or from single cells and protoplasts can be induced to form large numbers of roots, shoots, or embryo-like structures (embryoids). In this chapter we shall describe some of these morphogenetic phenomena and their applications, and also some of the problems which must still be overcome before full use can be made of these responses.

6.2. *The formation of organized structures*

6.2.1. *Root formation*

The most frequent type of recognizable morphogenesis occurring in cultured cells is root formation. This was first observed in 1939 by Nobécourt in carrot calluses, and has since been reported in numerous other plant tissues both on agar and in suspension culture (fig. 6.1 *a, b*). The earlier workers who studied this phenomenon demonstrated that it could be controlled, to some extent, by application of the auxin indolylacetic acid. Skoog's group showed that the ratio of auxin to kinetin in the culture medium was important in determining the type of morphogenesis exhibited by tobacco calluses (see Chapter 1).

In callus and suspension cultures of deadly nightshade initiated from explants of excised cultured roots, morphogenesis can be induced simply by transferring cells from the medium used for initiation and maintenance (Appendix: Table 2) to medium lacking naphthaleneacetic acid. The morphogenetic response of the cultures depends partly upon the previous cultural history of the excised roots used to initiate the cell cultures. Excised roots which have been cultured for numerous passages give rise to calluses and cell suspensions capable of forming large numbers of roots. Shoot formation can occasionally be observed, but is of very low frequency.

The root-forming cultures of nightshade are interesting in that roots develop in two distinct ways. First, these organs arise from

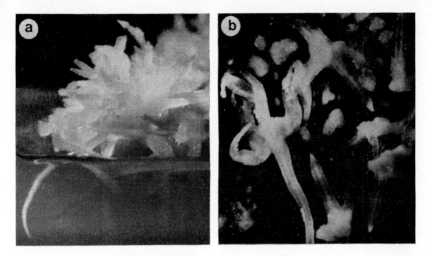

Fig. 6.1.   Root formation by cultured cells.   (*a*) *Allium cepa* callus (×4).
(*b*) *Atropa belladonna* suspension aggregates (×5).

peripheral meristematic cells of the suspension aggregates. In
maintenance medium containing naphthaleneacetic acid in which
root formation is suppressed, these aggregates consist of irregularly
shaped sub-units separated by intervening vacuolated cells (fig. 6.2 *a*).
After transfer to medium lacking this auxin, the sub-units separate
by breakdown of the vacuolated cells (fig. 6.2 *b*). The densely
cytoplasmic cells of the superficial layer of the aggregates form localized
regions of intensified meristematic activity which develop into root
primordia (fig. 6.2 *c, d*). Root formation can also occur without
the prior development of a continuous peripheral meristem. Small
groups of cytoplasmic cells within an aggregate organize to form
semi-circular meristems from which roots emerge (fig. 6.3 *a–d*).
Roots originating by these two pathways are released from the aggregates into the medium.   Their basal end generally shows an active
callus which continues to proliferate and to release further aggregates
with root forming ability into the suspension.
Many tissues exhibit root formation, but in most cultures this
organogenesis is too sporadic to afford any hopes of determining
the underlying biochemical conditions.   Nightshade cultures produce
very large numbers of roots, and it is possible to suppress and release
this ability by appropriate changes in the concentration of exogenous
naphthaleneacetic acid.   Unfortunately, the opportunity for detailed
biochemical studies is complicated by the fact that only a small
percentage of the total number of cells within the cultures is capable

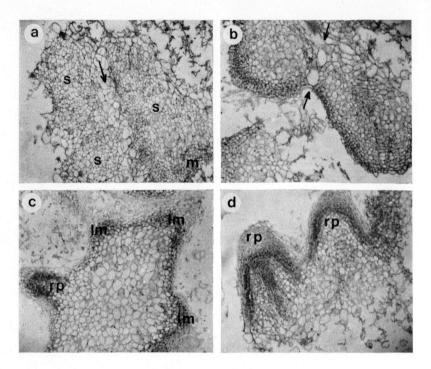

Fig. 6.2. Sections showing root development from *Atropa* suspension aggregates. (*a*) Aggregates composed of sub-units (s) separated by vacuolated cells (arrowed) after 21 days incubation in medium containing
2·0 mg/l NAA. m = peripheral meristematic zone. (*b*) Breakdown
of vacuolated cells resulting in a line of cleavage (arrowed) between
the sub-units after transfer to medium lacking auxin. (*c*) Localized
areas of meristematic activity (lm) in the peripheral zone which develop
into root primordia (rp). (*d*) Developing root primordia (× 50).

of producing roots, and such roots are formed from large multicellular
aggregates. Nevertheless, in this system it is possible to identify
macroscopically the potential root-forming aggregates by their
irregular shape and characteristic yellow-brown coloration. By
indices such as these, it has been possible to select out the aggregates
before, during, and after the formation of root primordia in an attempt
to correlate organogenesis with specific biosynthetic changes, such
as the conditions most favourable for the synthesis of important
belladonna alkaloids (see § 6.2.4). In the same way other workers
have measured qualitative and quantitative changes in enzymes
during root formation in an attempt to determine the nature of the
key processes occurring during morphogenesis.

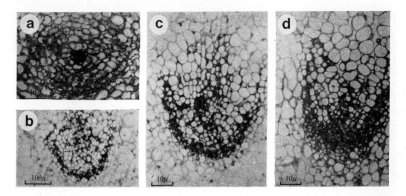

Fig. 6.3. (a) to (d). Stages in the development of a root primordium from an endogenous semi-circular meristem within an *Atropa* suspension aggregate.

6.2.2. *Shoot, plantlet, and embryoid formation*

As already stated, excised roots of nightshade which have been subcultured for numerous passages give rise to calluses and cell suspensions capable of forming large numbers of roots.   In contrast to this, tissues derived from recently excised cultured roots give rise to large numbers of plantlets, which develop either by shoot-bud formation, or by a process correctly described as embryogenesis.

Shoot-bud formation can occur in the absence of root formation to give structures similar to the one shown in fig. 6.4 *a*.   These can often be mistaken for embryoids.   More frequently shoot-buds develop upon roots initiated from cell aggregates.   The roots are released from the aggregates into the suspension, but the callus on their basal ends remains small and does not proliferate.   Instead it differentiates into a shoot-bud.   Normally the buds have two leaf-like structures (fig. 6.4 *b*), but sometimes there may be more and occasionally only a single leafy structure may develop.   These abnormalities in structure may reflect unstable genetics of the cultured cells.   However, intact seedlings grown in liquid culture may show similar abnormalities which suggests that the cultural conditions may cause these effects.

The same type of cell aggregate as that from which endogenous roots are initiated (those arising by the activity of internal meristems), can also give rise to embryoids.   These structures bear a striking resemblance to true zygotic embryos (fig. 6.5 *a, b*).   Sections of suspension aggregates undergoing embryogenesis indicate that embryoid development within the tissue proceeds by the transverse division of single, densely cytoplasmic cells into two cells of unequal size (fig. 6.6).   The larger cell, the suspensor initial, divides to form

101

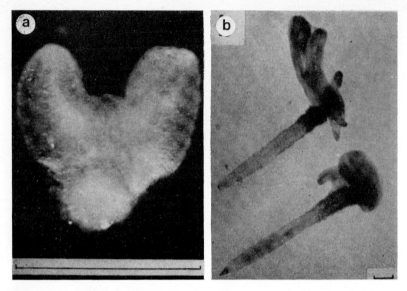

Fig. 6.4. Plantlet formation in *Atropa* suspensions. (*a*) A shoot-bud with two cotyledon-like structures. (*b*) Free-floating plantlets. Scale = 1 mm.

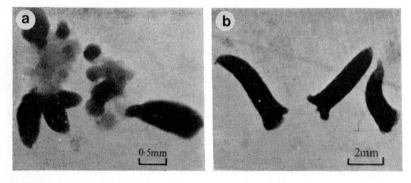

Fig. 6.5. Embryoids from *Atropa* suspensions. (*a*) Developing embryoids. (*b*) Free-floating, mature, torpedo-shaped embryoids.

the suspensor. The smaller cell, the embryonal initial, forms a small proembryonal mass which by further growth passes through globular, heart-shaped and torpedo-shaped stages similar to those observed in normal embryogeny. However, from the evidence obtained in studies of embryogenesis in cultured cells it cannot be said that the early segmentation patterns are similar to those normally occurring during zygotic embryogenesis. In a detailed study of embryogenic carrot cultures, A. A. McWilliam, S. M. Smith and H. E. Street found that the sequence of segmentations does not correspond with that described for zygotic embryogeny of the same species. Only when the developing embryoids are globular do they

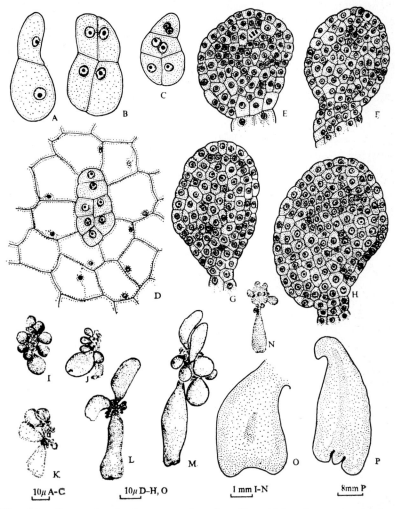

Fig. 6.6. Stages in development of embryoids within *Atropa* suspension aggregates. (*a*) to (*c*) Early stages in the development of a proembryoid. (*d*) Part of a cell aggregate showing an embedded proembryoid. (*e*) to (*h*) Progressive stages in development of a globular embryoid. (*i*) to (*n*) Cell aggregates from suspension culture showing various stages of embryogeny (diagrammatic). (*o*) and (*p*) Later stages in embryogeny (diagrammatic).

103

closely resemble the zygotic embryo. These workers suggest that studies in cell culture raise the important question of whether the cellular pattern is " subordinate to the integrated polarized growth and development of the young embryo as a whole ". This would permit " considerable flexibility and modification by environmental factors, of the early pro-embryo stages without impairing the origin of a normal embryo and seedling ". Extensive studies on zygotic embryology have led to complex classifications of types of segmentation patterns and even to a series of laws which are said to regulate the sequence, position, and fate of the cells in the embryo. Detailed descriptions of these patterns can be obtained in any textbook of plant embryology, references to which will be found in the book by C. W. Wardlaw (see reading list). Closer examination of embryology *in vivo* clearly indicates that embryos of numerous higher plants appear to show anomalous patterns of formation in their early stages, even though the fully-formed embryo is morphologically normal. H. A. Borthwick points out significant deviations in segmentation patterns in zygotic embryos of carrot, and has shown that variations exist in the fate of the cells of a 4-celled stage. The patterns observable in cultured cells may simply reflect the patterns which can also occur in the zygote, and should not be considered as abnormal.

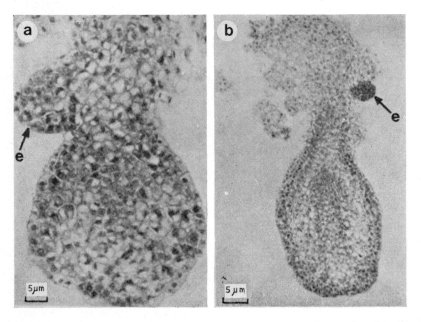

Fig. 6.7. Developing *Atropa* embryoids showing adventive embryoids (e) arising on their suspensors.

Another interesting feature of the embryogenic deadly nightshade cells is that embryogenesis can also occur from the suspensors of the embryoids themselves. Embryoids formed from suspensor cells differ from the first-formed embryoids in that they lack a suspensor and have a broad-base attachment to the suspensor of the first-formed embryoids (fig. 6.7 *a*, *b*).

For the formation of shoots, plantlets, and embryoids the newly isolated roots and the cell cultures subsequently initiated from them should be grown on media containing elevated levels of ammonium ions, e.g. 2·37 g ammonium sulphate per litre of medium, followed by transfer to medium lacking naphthaleneacetic acid. Even under these conditions, tissues derived from older, serially sub-cultured excised roots still form large numbers of roots, and shoot formation is of low frequency. This suggests that there is a difference between recently excised roots and those that have been maintained in culture for some time. This difference is reflected in the morphogenetic expression of the calluses and the cell suspensions derived from them.

In view of the capacity of excised cultured roots to produce shoots directly (Chapter 3), a capacity which also declines on serial sub-culture, it is tempting to speculate that excised roots maintained in culture for different periods of time contain different amounts of specific shoot-forming compounds. It is possible that these compounds, or different synthetic capacities for the synthesis of these compounds, are carried over into the initial cell cultures and are responsible for the observed morphogenetic expression. In the absence of identification of the unknown factors involved, such a view is difficult to accept. The addition of kinetin to excised root cultures of woad (*Isatis tinctoria*) can restore a declining capacity of the roots to form shoot-buds, but whether endogenous cytokinins are responsible for the observed differences between cultures of different origin in the nightshade system is open to argument. The studies nevertheless demonstrate that caution must be exercised in deciding whether a particular morphogenetic response induced in cultured cells is primarily caused by the components of the culture medium, by compounds actually present within the cultured tissues, or by compounds carried over from the initial explant. The problem demands that specific endogenous morphogenetic compounds be isolated and identified which can induce the growth and morphogenesis of isolated single cells.

6.2.3. *Cellular differentiation*

In 1963, R. H. Wetmore and J. P. Rier showed that cellular differentiation could be induced in calluses by application of auxin (indolylacetic acid or naphthaleneacetic acid) and sucrose. When introduced

105

H

into a cone-like depression cut in the upper surface of the tissue, these compounds moved from the cone into the callus, causing a tissue pattern to develop. The pattern has been interpreted as representing an imperfect reproduction of the tissue pattern of the stem. Transverse sections of the callus in the region of cellular differentiation showed that separate strands of conducting tissue cells were formed in a circular pattern, each strand connected by lines of dividing cells bearing a resemblance to interfascicular cambium. In addition, the conducting strands were composed of cells bearing a resemblance to xylem elements and others to phloem cells. If the level of auxin was increased and that of sucrose lowered, only the xylem-like elements were formed. These experiments demonstrated that callus cells can respond in a similar manner to cells of the intact plant, and the manner in which this response is expressed is determined by the position of the cells in relation to gradients of compounds inducive to growth. Cultured cells can thus recapitulate the pattern of growth exhibited by cells in the intact plant.

Observations of cellular differentiation and embryogenesis clearly indicate the potential totipotency of some plant cells. As a result of these findings, workers became excited by the possibility that one might be able to convert single cells of a suspension to specialized cells of a particular type. Such a system would be extremely attractive for studies of cellular differentiation. Furthermore, if certain secondary plant products such as the belladonna alkaloids and other drugs, are synthesized by specific cells of the plant body, such a system would find tremendous application in the large-scale production of compounds useful to man. Unfortunately, to achieve this aim has proved to be an extremely difficult task. The degrees of morphological cellular differentiation that have been observed in culture have been seen in callus tissues or in the aggregates which are always found in suspension cultures. This may suggest that cell contact may be necessary to provide the appropriate environment for cell differentiation to occur, at least cellular differentiation as it occurs in the intact plant. Perhaps other cells provide the necessary source and sink of essential metabolites, or such an environment may be necessary to set up certain unknown physical conditions.

Recently Kohlenbach and B. Schmidt has obtained evidence suggesting that single isolated leaf mesophyll cells of certain plants *can* give rise to tracheidlike cells in the absence of aggregation and division. Such a finding, when reproducible *en masse* will be of great consequence for cellular differentiation studies.

6.2.4. *The biosynthesis of secondary plant products by cultured cells*
It was in an attempt to gain some understanding of cellular differentiation and secondary product biosynthesis that cultures of

deadly nightshade were first initiated. This plant produces tropane alkaloids, including atropine, which have a use in medicine. The production of the alkaloids within the whole plant is in many instances localized, and the amounts of each alkaloid and their distribution within the plant often change in a characteristic manner during development. This suggests that pathways for alkaloid biosynthesis may depend upon tissue and cell differentiation within the synthesizing organs. In nightshade cultures, alkaloids could only be detected in excised cultured roots and in plants and plantlets derived from callus or cell suspensions. They could not be detected in shoots or callus and cell suspension cultures in the absence of roots. In suspensions it was possible to identify and separate the aggregates forming roots. Alkaloids were only detected when the aggregates possessed roots, indicating that conditions favouring alkaloid biosynthesis could only be achieved in association with root organization.

There have been reports that secondary product biosynthesis has been achieved in the absence of organogenesis. For example, M. H. Zenk and his co-workers have found that suspension cultures of *Morinda citrifolia* (Indian mulberry) produce considerably larger amounts of anthraquinone than the roots of the intact plant. Generally, however, secondary products are formed in unorganized cell cultures in extremely small amounts, or in a form which differs from the required product. In a recent review, H. E. Street (1973) has suggested that mutant selection techniques may prove more rewarding for the study of cellular differentiation and for exploiting biosynthetic potentialities of cultured cells than techniques aimed at reproducing the factors which control differentiation in the intact plant. This view implies that it should be possible to open up morphological or biochemical differentiation pathways either by inactivating compounds that repress these processes, or by inactivating genes responsible for the synthesis of the repressor molecules. The availability of haploid cells by the culture of pollen grains (Chapter 7), makes such advances a real possibility in the immediate future.

6.3. *Factors controlling morphogenesis in culture*

6.3.1. *De-differentiation and totipotency*

The phenomenon of de-differentiation during callus induction from explants is of great interest, since a precise understanding of the changes accompanying this process may go a long way towards answering many questions in morphogenesis. During de-differentiation, successive cell divisions in mature cells are believed to result in the removal of inhibitors of gene action, until eventually derivative cells are taken to a ground state. In this state the cells once again become able to express their totipotency, that is to exhibit a specific morphogenetic response via root, shoot, or embryoid formation, or by their development into specialized cell types. In cases where meristematic cells are obtained but where totipotency is not expressed, which is of quite common occurrence in plant tissue cultures, it can be argued that because of unsatisfactory cultural conditions the removal of gene inhibitors has been incomplete. This view clearly implies that cell differentiation is a process whereby the genetic information present in the original fertilized egg is progressively repressed but remains structurally unchanged. The degree of repression depends upon the position of the cells within the plant body, and therefore upon the particular functions which they are called upon to perform. In other words, a cell in a root and a cell in a shoot are different in their morphology and biochemistry only by virtue of their position; basically both are identical. Workers who uphold this theory base their argument upon the fact that in certain species callus cultures can be initiated from virtually any plant part (root, shoot, leaf, flowers and so on), and regardless of their origin all calluses become capable of producing embryoids. Critics of this argument point out that there is no evidence to suggest that all cells in the plant body are totipotent. They consider that even in species where callus cultures initiated from different parts of the plant produce embryoids, the number of embryoids is small compared to the total number of cells within the culture. Generally, very large explants are used to initiate the cultures, and it is possible that only certain cell types within the explants are responsible for producing the cells which in culture give rise to embryoids. The bulk of the cultures may be derived from cells which have been genetically altered during differentiation. Even in cases where embryoids are produced, many are imperfect. This could be interpreted as meaning that cells responsible for their formation may not be perfectly totipotent.

6.3.2. *Cell isolation*

It has been postulated that one of the factors in determining the expression of totipotency is the release of a single cell from the influence of other cells. The fact remains that even though there is a large body of evidence indicating that embryoids can arise from single cells in callus and cell suspensions, no one has been able to observe the growth of a single cell directly into an embryoid without an intervening callus phase. The possibility therefore exists that embryoids can also be formed by the association together of more than one cell. This is suggested by the broad-base attachment of the suspensor-derived embryoids in nightshade cultures. The evidence with this system emphasizes the importance of the multicellular aggregate in determining morphogenetic expression. This view is further substantiated in studies carried out with *Ranunculus sceleratus*. In a series of studies R. N. Konar and K. Nataraja showed that callus cultures derived from vegetative or floral organs of this species give rise to large numbers of embryoids, which arise from superficial cells of the callus. These embryoids develop into plantlets either *in situ* or when teased out and transferred to fresh medium. The plantlets may themselves initiate embryoids along their hypocotyl surfaces. Such stem embryoids arise from single epidermal cells and display the two, four, six, eight celled, globular, heart-shaped and mature stages of embryogeny (Fig. 6.8). This phenomenon has also been observed on stems of microspore-derived plantlets of the commercially important plant *Brassica napus* (rape). Because the embryoids arise from single epidermal cells it should be possible to subject stems to the effects of mutagenic agents and in this way obtain mutant plants very rapidly (see Chapter 7).

One of the factors which has been implicated as important in determining the expression of totipotency in single cells is the severing of protoplasmic continuity between adjacent cells by the breaking of plasmodesmatal connections. However, in *Ranunculus* it has been demonstrated by electron microscopy that cells embarking on embryogenesis retain these connections with adjacent epidermal cells of the stem. Only later, when the proembryoid is multicellular, is it clearly delimited from the surrounding tissues. In fact, the initial nurture of the embryoids may be provided by protoplasmic continuity between the embryonic cells and the surrounding tissues. The extremely complex nature of callus or cell suspension cultures makes it difficult to draw conclusions as to whether embryoids arise from single cells or by association together of more than one cell. Indirect evidence suggests that embryoids can arise from single cells within callus aggregates of deadly nightshade and *Ranunculus sceleratus*.

An ultrastructural comparison has been made of epidermal and callus cells of *Ranunculus* undergoing embryogenesis. Cells of the young stem proembryoid bear a striking resemblance to the highly cytoplasmic superficial cells of callus aggregates. A characteristic feature of the embryogenic cells of different origin is that they both contain large numbers of vesicles in their cytoplasm adjacent to the cell wall. In cells of developing epidermal embryoids there may be so many as to give the cytoplasm a honeycomb appearance. As a result of these studies it has been suggested that these vesicles contain lipid reserves important for the growth of embryoids into plantlets, or that they may be important in the transport of substances from the cell surface into the cell. After protoplasmic continuity is severed such a metabolism could provide a means of transport of essential metabolites from the stem or from the callus aggregate into the developing embryoid.

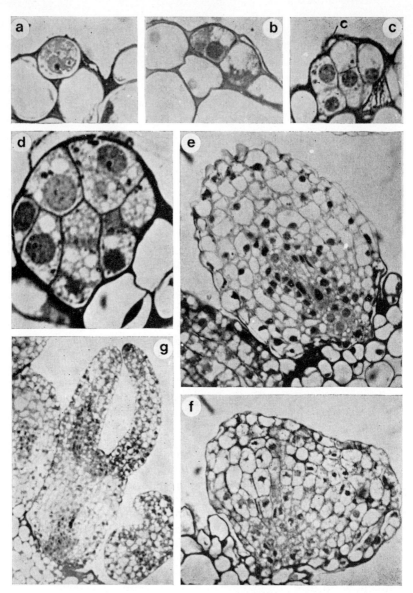

Fig. 6.8. Stages in development of embryoids from epidermal cells of the hypocotyl of *Ranunculus sceleratus* plantlets. (*a*) A single cytoplasm-rich epidermal cell. (*b*) A pair of such cells ($\times 660$). (*c*) Two 2-celled proembryoids and a single cytoplasm-rich epidermal cell. c = cuticle ($\times 660$). (*d*) Oblique section through a young embryoid ($\times 1200$). (*e*) Late globular proembryoid showing a central core of meristematic cells ($\times 280$). (*f*) Heart-shaped proembryoid ($\times 280$). (*g*) Mature embryoid showing cotyledons and root and shoot apices. ($\times 250$).

6.3.3. Chemical agents

In Chapter 1 we described the classical tobacco system in which it is possible to control root and shoot formation by adjusting the ratios of auxin to cytokinin. Unfortunately, there is little evidence to support the principle that morphogenesis in culture is controlled by shifts in the ratio of plant growth substances. On the other hand, the results do not disprove this view. We have briefly discussed how the situation is complicated by unknown regulators which may be present in the explants used to initiate the tissue cultures. It is possible that the nature and quantity of such compounds differ from species to species, and even from explant to explant of the same species. The omission of auxin (naphthaleneacetic acid) from the culture medium for deadly nightshade permits the tissues to undergo morphogenesis. This suggests that naphthaleneacetic acid is acting as a morphogenetic inhibitor, and that when it is removed from the medium morphogenesis occurs in an orderly fashion at the expense of compounds endogenously synthesized by large cell aggregates. Inorganic and organic nitrogen compounds, e.g. potassium and ammonium salts, amino acids and amides, have also been cited as being important in controlling morphogenesis in culture. Although their effect can be very marked, we know virtually nothing of how this is achieved. Do they act directly in morphogenesis, or do they affect the synthesis of some other compounds which then act in morphogenesis? Do they exert their effect by controlling osmotic pressure, hydrogen ion concentration, or membrane permeability? The finding that plant cells can be totipotent has opened up a completely new field of investigation into these problems. Such questions as those outlined must be answered before we can begin to understand the complex nature of living systems.

6.4. Loss of morphogenetic capacity in cultured cells

The problem of not knowing the nature of the cells within the original explant, or the nature of compounds carried over from the explant into cell culture, brings to light another phenomenon of wide occurrence in plant tissue culture. When calluses or cell suspensions are maintained for long periods by sub-culture, their initial ability to undergo morphogenesis is lost or considerably reduced under the same cultural conditions. This is true whether morphogenesis is exhibited by root or shoot formation or by embryogenesis. The causes for this changing morphogenetic expression are not known, although numerous theories have been advanced. It has been suggested that unorganized growth results in genetic instability, since cultured cells frequently contain nuclei showing various degrees of polyploidy, aneuploidy, and chromosome mutation. This instability is then assumed to lead to a change in, and an ultimate loss of, morphogenetic capacity. Such a view is acceptable in cases where complete chromosomes have been eliminated from the genome of the cells, e.g. in aneuploidy, but at the present time there is no evidence which convincingly correlates loss of morphogenesis with polyploidy, a phenomenon of widespread occurrence in cultured cells. In fact, experimental results indicate that highly polyploid plantlets can be regenerated from cell cultures. A possibility that has not been explored in many cases where morphogenetic capacity has apparently been lost and where polyploidy is pronounced, is that cells of different ploidy levels may require different cultural conditions for this capacity to be exposed. Furthermore, in many cases where high degrees of polyploidy have been observed in cultured tissues, this does not necessarily indicate cytological instability of the cultures. Large explants possibly containing cells with highly polyploid nuclei may have been used to initiate the cultures, and it is conceivable that with continuous propagation such cells may be selected at the expense of diploid cells. Some cultured systems are genetically unstable, but such findings cannot be extended to include tissues of all species.

Another possible cause of the decline in morphogenetic expression may be a changing physiology of the cultures. In a recent review, J. Reinert (1973) gives examples of carrot calluses in which their morphogenetic capacity on a certain culture medium had apparently been lost. This was restored when the cultures were transferred to another medium of high nitrogen content. Such a result could only be explained on a physiological basis. A similar view was reached in studies of nightshade cultures. The evidence with this tissue suggests that the morphogenetic ability and the type of morphogenesis are at first determined by unknown factors present in the initial explant. During sub-culture the suspensions change from a finely dispersed state to forming large aggregates; morphogenesis is confined to these cell clumps. Only if such organized aggregates proliferate faster than other apparently non-competent cells within the culture can morphogenetic potential be retained. However, because of their organization, the aggregates proliferate more slowly, with the result that on continuous sub-culture the population reverts to a finely dispersed suspension with no apparent morphogenetic potential. The latter is retained if aggregates are taken out from the suspension, fragmented, and recultured. Nightshade cultures which have apparently lost their morphogenetic ability have been subjected to single-cell cloning techniques, and clones have been obtained that are capable of morphogenesis. This suggests either that competent cells are still present within the cultures, or, as in the carrot system, that the apparently non-competent cells are perfectly competent under the correct conditions. Such studies demonstrate the need to obtain single-cell clones of known genetics and to attempt to grow them under conditions where aggregation and fluctuations in the nutrient conditions are minimal. It remains to be seen whether it will be possible to retain the morphogenetic potentialities of cultured cells for indefinite periods by the use of chemostat and turbidostat culture systems.

6.5. *Applications of the morphogenetic potential of cultured cells*

The finding that some plant cells are totipotent has provided a completely new approach to studies in morphogenesis and differentiation. In addition, this discovery has provided a new way of breeding plants and a means for their propagation.

6.5.1. *Plant breeding*

The variation encountered in cultured cells and in plantlets regenerated from them is generally undesirable in most investigations. However, this variation may provide an opportunity to obtain new and important genotypes which can be used in plant breeding programmes. It should be possible to increase the variation still further by the use of mutagenic agents. Workers at the Volcani Centre, Israel, have been applying mutagenic treatments to callus and cell suspension

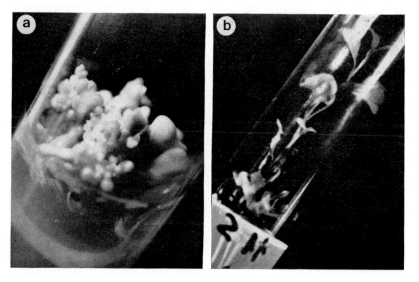

Fig. 6.9. *Citrus sinensis.* (*a*) Highly embryonic nucellar callus, showing large cotyledonary embryoids and numerous smaller pseudobulbils. (*b*) Plantlet which has arisen from an embryoid.

cultures derived from the nucellus of the orange. Since these cultures form large numbers of embryoids which can be grown into plants (fig. 6.9 *a*, *b*), it should be possible to propagate any valuable mutants which are obtained. Recent techniques for the isolation of single cells and protoplasts directly from the plant and for the induction of their growth, provide ideal systems for mutagenic studies. Thus, if leaves or other plant organs are irradiated or treated with mutagenic chemicals, and cells or protoplasts isolated from these organs are plated on to selective media, it should be possible to isolate new genotypes resistant to specific chemical compounds or physical conditions. Unfortunately, the use of mutagens on normal diploid or polyploid plants is hampered by the presence of more than one copy of the same gene. The finding that microspores can be induced to grow in culture to produce haploid callus or plantlets or both overcomes this problem. This application will be discussed in more detail in Chapter 7.

Brief mention has already been made of attempts to introduce macromolecules, organelles, and micro-organisms into isolated protoplasts. If such foreign bodies are retained, replicated, and transmitted through cell division to cell derivatives of the protoplast, it may be possible to obtain modified cell types. The development of techniques for fusing isolated plant protoplasts also provides an opportunity to obtain hybrid cells from sexually incompatible species. If the hybrid cells can be induced to undergo shoot regeneration, these plants may be completely new and of possible commercial value.

6.5.2. *Plant propagation.*

Many important plants grown from seed show tremendous variation in growth, habit, and yield, and it is often necessary for the grower to select from the varied population those that possess some excellent qualities, and to propagate them vegetatively. For some plants, e.g. the oil-palm (*Elaeis guineensis*), there may be no known method of vegetative propagation, and in others the conventional propagation techniques may be so slow that it may take many years before the quality of any newly discovered lines can be passed on to the consumer, and then usually at an extremely high price. It is for plants such as these that tissue culture is well-suited. Orchids for example, are popular both as house-plants and as cut flowers, yet they are very expensive. One of the reasons for their cost is that orchid seeds are often very difficult and sometimes impossible to germinate by conventional methods, and so for many years they have been germinated aseptically on culture media before being transferred to potting compost. The seedlings often take several years to reach maturity, and then many have to be discarded because the quality of their flowers may be too poor for commercial release. The procedure was to select from the varied population high quality plants, and then to propagate them by conventional means, a process which at the best gives only a few additional plants per year. A major advance came about in 1960 when G. Morel, while attempting to induce meristem growth of the orchid *Cymbidium* with the object of producing virus-free plants, showed that the meristems have the capacity to form a mass of tissue, morphologically similar to the protocorms which are formed when orchid seeds germinate *in vitro*. Morel later showed that this tissue could be divided into one or more pieces, and each piece could be transferred to fresh culture medium and induced to form further protocorm-like structures. Using this technique, it is possible to produce very large numbers of the embryonic structures very rapidly. Each protocorm can be grown into a plant which will be, excluding mutation, exactly like the parent plant and will flower in the same way as the parent. Since Morel's pioneer studies, several laboratories throughout the world have been applying the technique to *Cymbidium* and to several other orchid genera. Fig. 6.10 shows proliferating protocorms from the genus *Cattleya* which have formed after three months culture of a shoot tip. Tissue culture methods should bring the

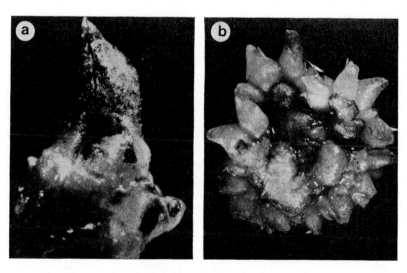

Fig. 6.10. Propagation of the orchid *Cattleya* by the use of shoot-tip explants. (*a*) Shoot-tip after one month in culture proliferating to give protocorms (×15). (*b*) A large number of protocorms formed after three months culture. Each protocorm can produce further protocorms, or can be induced to form plantlets (×10).

115

price of orchids within a range required to make them far more popular throughout the world.

Similar techniques are now being applied to the oil-palm and to other commercially important plants. Reports have already appeared that some commercial laboratories have successfully produced plantlets from oil-palm callus, which is an excellent demonstration of the potentialities offered by tissue culture techniques. Unfortunately, there are still numerous problems to be overcome. The orchid meristem system is one which retains a high degree of organization, and there is little difficulty in maintaining indefinite proliferation of the cultures or in obtaining the desired plant product. If one attempts to repeat the process through unorganized callus or cell suspension culture, quite commonly the morphogenetic capacity of the culture is lost, or the regenerated products are genetically different from the original parent type. However, this is not always the case. Very recently E. De Laughe and E. De Bruijne reported the results of their studies with calluses from different species of tomato (*Lycopersicon esculentum* and *L. peruvianum*). They found that callus tissue maintained for a year over 30 sub-cultures retained its original organogenetic capacity. More than 200 plants obtained from the calluses were screened for possible genetic variation, but none could be observed; phenotypically the plants were identical to the donor species. Since these workers also observed no segregation in the seed progeny of the callus-derived plants, they concluded that no genetic aberrations occurred throughout the culture period. Their results are also interesting because they found that application of 2-chloroethyltrimethylammonium chloride (CCC) to plants prior to culture enabled the level of hormones required in the medium to be reduced. Similarly, W. F. Sheridan has reported phenotypic stability in plants regenerated from callus of *Lilium* which had been maintained for seven years *in vitro*. *Lilium* callus is grown and plantlets regenerated on medium free of vitamins, inositol, and hormones. The same is also true of two-year-old cultures of Shamouti Orange (fig. 6.9 *a*, *b*). It appears that when tissue culture techniques are applied to plant propagation the use of high concentrations of growth substances should be avoided. Although hormones increase proliferation, they can cause abnormalities in the cells and in plants regenerated from the cells. In the future it should be possible to develop growth media containing levels of inorganic salts which stimulate the endogenous synthesis of natural regulators. A similar effect may be achieved by pretreatment of the donor plants with compounds such as CCC. In this way it may be possible to avoid the use of exogenous regulators, while allowing proliferation to occur in an organized manner.

An alternative possibility to callus and cell suspension culture techniques would be to develop methods to induce cells isolated directly from plant meristems to undergo embryoid formation without first forming a callus. The recent finding that single-celled microspores can give rise directly to embryoids, suggests that this may soon be possible for vegetative cells. Such a development would have very important consequences, and would avoid many of the problems currently inherent in plant tissue culture.

6.6. *Summary*

In this chapter we have described some of the types of morphogenetic response which can be induced in cultured cells, particularly as they relate to the brilliant postulates of Haberlandt. The finding that differentiated plant cells are totipotent has realized his theories. However, at this stage in the development of tissue culture techniques, there is no evidence to suggest that all cells of the plant body retain their totipotency after differentiation. We have briefly described some of the biochemical and ultrastructural studies which have been carried out with cultured systems. We also felt it necessary to consider in detail some of the problems which exist in this field. They are not intended to be a criticism of this area of plant tissue culture, but their appreciation is necessary because they emphasize the need to develop new methods and new ideas to solve many very fundamental problems in plant science.

Tissue cultures obtained from complex explants are heterogeneous and can give heterogeneous responses. This morphogenetic response is apparently lost on continued sub-culture. There is a fundamental requirement to obtain large populations of uniformly totipotent single cells of known genetics, and to determine the factors necessary for the expression of totipotency without the complications of cellular aggregation. Only when this has been achieved can full use be made of the unique opportunities offered by the potential totipotency of plant cells.

CHAPTER 7
the culture of haploid reproductive cells

7.1. *Introduction*

RECENT studies have shown that it is possible to induce the growth in culture of haploid microspores (immature pollen grains before they contain male gametes), and of tissue derived from haploid macrospores (megaspores or embryo sacs). This finding is likely in the immediate future to contribute substantially to studies on the genetic control of plant growth and metabolism, and it should also, if properly utilized, greatly assist plant breeding programmes. In certain species of angiosperms it has been demonstrated that single-celled microspores can develop directly into embryoids without an intervening callus phase. This opens up the possibility of determining the factors which may induce a similar response in single isolated vegetative plant cells or protoplasts. Microspores and macrospores arise by meiosis, and this process has several important consequences relevant to the discussion which follows. Consequently, we shall briefly describe some of the important parts of the process.

7.2. *Meiosis and its significance*

In a diploid cell the chromosomes exist in homologous pairs, one member of each pair having been contributed by a pollen grain and the other member by the egg during fertilization. The genes, which are responsible for controlling biochemically specific genetic traits, are also formed in pairs known as allelic pairs, each allele being present on one of the pair of homologous chromosomes. Although each allele controls the same genetic trait as the other allele, it may be able to control a different phenotypic expression of that trait. A diploid cell with two identical alleles is homozygous for that particular gene; if the alleles differ the cell is heterozygous for the gene. When the activity of only one of the alleles is expressed phenotypically in a heterozygote, the allele is said to be dominant. The activity of the allele which is not expressed phenotypically (the recessive allele), will remain undetected until it is separated from the dominant allele. Such a separation occurs during meiosis. The first step in meiosis is the synthesis of a new copy of genetic material. Following this duplication, each chromosome can be seen to consist of two distinct strands or sister chromatids. Then each duplicated chromosome

118

pairs with its homologous chromosome. During this process the duplicated homologous chromosomes are in intimate contact at various points along their length. These points or chiasmata represent points at which two non-sister chromatids have undergone an exchange of parts. This exchange is of great importance because it produces new gene combinations. At the first meiotic division, the duplicated partners separate or segregate, and at the second division, the sister chromatids segregate. As a result four haploid nuclei are produced from a single diploid nucleus. During meiosis allelic genes are segregated, are produced in new combinations with other alleles, and are represented only as single copies in the meiotic products, and because of this the discovery that microspores and macrospores can be grown in culture is likely to be extremely important. Haploid cells in combination with mutation techniques, single-cell cloning, protoplast culture, and plant regeneration, provide a unique opportunity to study the metabolism and genetics of higher plants. As haploid cells contain only single gene copies, mutagenic treatments can be used to modify or eliminate undesirable genes without the complications of their alleles. Such studies lead to a greater understanding of the processes involved in the regulation of growth and cellular differentiation. This may lead also to the establishment of cell lines capable of producing large amounts of economically important secondary products such as gums, resins, alkaloids, flavourings, enzymes, and so on. Furthermore, by using haploid tissue it should be possible to obtain valuable normal or mutant homozygous plant lines which could be incorporated into plant breeding programmes.

7.3. *The culture of tissue derived from gymnosperm megaspores*

In gymnosperms, the single megasporocyte (megaspore mother cell) of each ovule is deeply seated within the tissue of the nucellus. Following meiosis only one of the megaspores is functional, and the other three soon disintegrate. The single megaspore enlarges and a series of free nuclear divisions occurs to produce the primary endosperm or megagametophyte. Ultimately, this haploid female gametophyte becomes a massive cellular body. As the tissue originates from a single haploid megaspore and is easy to isolate aseptically and free of any diploid tissue, it is an attractive source of material from which to obtain haploid tissue and/or gymnosperm plantlets. O. Huhtinen has successfully induced callus formation from female gametophyte tissue of the Norway spruce (*Picea abies*) on a culture medium containing 2,4-D and kinetin. He found that although it was possible to initiate cultures from mature megagametophyte tissue, a higher success rate (0·1 to 1·0 per cent) could be achieved by culturing tissue immediately after most of its mitotic activity had ceased. At

119

this stage the gametophyte tissue begins to accumulate starch and to change from liquid to solid. It is normally extremely difficult to induce organ formation from calluses of woody species. However, Huhtinen found that by altering the auxin/kinetin ratio of his culture medium it was possible to induce the formation of numerous bud-like structures, some of which produced several cotyledons similar to embryos of this species. Attempts to initiate roots on the shoots have so far been unsuccessful, but it is probably only a matter of time before this is achieved. Such techniques may lead to important advances in the breeding of forest trees.

7.4. *The growth of microspores in culture*

Microspores can be induced to grow by two methods. First they can be cultured while still enclosed within the anther, and until very recently this was the only way to induce their growth. The second method is to isolate the microspores from the anther and to culture them by techniques similar to those already described for single vegetative cells and protoplasts.

7.4.1. *The culture of anther-enclosed microspores*

The technique is basically very simple. Unopened flower buds or inflorescences are usually surface-sterilized, and the tissue surrounding the reproductive organs is removed. The anthers are then excised and placed on the surface of a culture medium. The medium should have a composition which selects for the growth of microspores at the expense of the somatic cells present in the filament, connective and anther wall. In some species, for example deadly nightshade and tobacco, a medium lacking growth hormones may be suitable. In most other successful species growth of the microspores can be achieved by adding to the medium appropriate concentrations of auxins, cytokinins and/or various complexes such as coconut milk. The response of the microspores varies from species to species and as discussed later, this response is dependent upon numerous factors other than the composition of the culture medium. They undergo embryogenesis or callus formation.

7.4.1.1. *Embryogenesis*

Although the number of species which produce embryoids from cultured microspores is small, e.g. deadly nightshade, *Brassica napus*, *Datura* spp., *Nicotiana* sp., rye (*Secale cereale*), this list is slowly increasing, which may indicate that the phenomenon is of universal occurrence. In *Nicotiana tabacum*, J. P. Nitsch and his co-workers showed that when anthers were aseptically removed from flower buds in which the petals were the same length as the sepals, the microspores within the anthers could be induced to form embryoids. The anthers were cultured on the medium given in Appendix Table 6 and then incubated at 28°C by day and 22°C by night under low light intensity. Three to four weeks later embryoids and plantlets emerged from some of the anthers (fig. 7.1 *a*). After the plantlets had developed an adequate root system they were transplanted to potting compost and raised to maturity. Chromosome counts made on roots of the plants showed many to be haploid. A further

Fig. 7.1. Embryogenesis from cultured anthers of: (*a*) *Nicotiana tabacum* (×12). (*b*) *Brassica napus* (×30). In *Nicotiana* large numbers of microspore embryoids can be produced in a responsive anther. In *Brassica* anthers only a few microspores are embryonic and often only one embryoid is produced from a responsive anther.

indication of their haploid nature was that after flowering the plants failed to set seed, as they were sterile. Additional studies have shown that certain microspores within the anther produce during culture a round mass of cells which eventually ruptures the microspore wall. The mass of cells represents a globular stage of embryogenesis which subsequently develops through the typical heart-shaped, torpedo-shaped and cotyledonary stages.

121

Species within the genus *Nicotiana* produce large numbers of plant-lets directly from microspores via embryogenesis. Species within some other genera produce embryoids only with difficulty. *Brassica napus* for example, can form embryoids from cultured anthers (fig. 7.1 *b*), but commonly only one anther from several hundreds cultured is responsive. Further, in this plant only very few of the microspores within the cultured anthers actually develop into embryoids. Cultured anthers of rye can be induced to produce embryoids, plantlets or calluses (fig. 7.2 *a–d*). Success in this species followed only after numerous experiments, involving many thousands of anthers, were carried out.

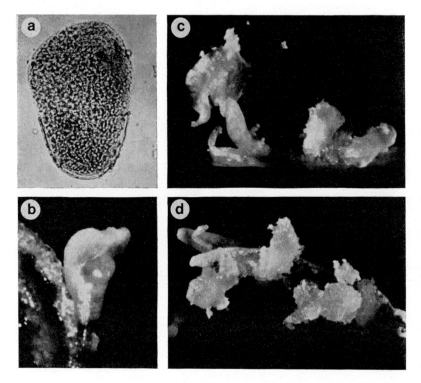

Fig. 7.2. Morphogenesis from microspores in cultured anthers of *Secale cereale*. All photographs are of structures observed in anthers cultured for three weeks on Nitsch and Nitsch medium (Appendix Table 6) containing 0·25 mg 2,4-D l^{-1} and subsequently transferred for a further three weeks to a medium with Murashige and Skoog's salts (Appendix Table 5) and the same concentration of 2,4-D. Embryoids (*a*) and (*b*), plantlets (*c*), and calluses (*d*) can be formed. The young embryoid in (*a*) still possesses part of the original microspore wall.

7.4.1.2. Callus formation

In many genera microspore growth produces a callus rather than an embryoid. This is true for plants such as wild cabbage (*Brassica oleracea*) and barley. The view has been put forward that the first divisions within growing microspores may be highly organized and can result in embryoid formation. However, because of unsatisfactory conditions in the medium the young embryoid later proliferates and gives rise to a callus. This implies that although the initial culture medium may be suitable for inducing the first stages of embryogenesis, the developing embryoids must be immediately transferred to another to prevent callus formation. In rye, calluses and embryoids can sometimes be found within the same anther. Some of the calluses are clearly derived from proliferating embryoids, but it is more difficult to account for the origin of others. Consequently, the possibility that different microspores may have different morphogenetic pathways under identical cultural conditions should not be overlooked.

Many problems may be encountered in regenerating plantlets from the callus derived from microspores. This is true for example, in tomato. Even when plantlets are regenerated from the calluses they may be highly abnormal. An instance of this is the frequent occurrence of albino plantlets from microspore calluses of barley. In such cases it is difficult to decide whether the albino plantlets have arisen from abnormal microspores or whether the abnormalities arise during the growth of unorganized callus. Another problem is that any calluses formed from anther cultures may be heterogeneous, since probably more than one microspore will contribute to their formation. As briefly mentioned in Chapter 6, plantlets formed from calluses or cell suspensions may arise not from single cells but by the union of more than one cell. Plantlets arising from heterogeneous microspore calluses may therefore be genetically non-uniform (chimaeras). A direct approach to overcome these problems would be to attempt to produce embryoids directly from microspores, and preferably from microspores that are completely isolated from the anther.

7.4.2. The culture of isolated microspores

The technique of culturing isolated microspores avoids the possible involvement of somatic tissue in plantlet formation. The first successful culture of angiosperm pollen was obtained by T. Kameya and K. Hinata in 1970 with mature pollen from *Brassica* species. Using a liquid culture medium containing 10–15 per cent sucrose and 10 per cent coconut milk, they were able to induce the formation of small cell colonies. The latter were capable of only limited growth and plantlets could not be obtained. Two years later, W. R. Sharp, R. S. Raskin and H. E. Sommer obtained callus clones from single microspores of tomato. Their technique was to isolate the microspores in liquid medium and then to pipette small numbers on to filter paper discs maintained in direct contact with cultured anthers of the same plant (Muir's paper raft technique). The anthers acted as a nurse tissue, producing compounds which diffused through the filter paper and which promoted the single microspores to grow. About the same time C. Nitsch was extending her experiments on *Datura*, *Nicotiana* and other genera. She showed that extracts prepared from cultured anthers containing developing multicellular structures could induce embryogenesis when added to medium used for culturing microspores. The extract was analysed and from the results it was possible to devise a completely synthetic medium for the culture of isolated tobacco pollen (fig. 7.3). Compared with the medium used for the culture of tobacco anthers (Appendix Table 6), the medium for isolated tobacco pollen contains 5 g l^{-1}

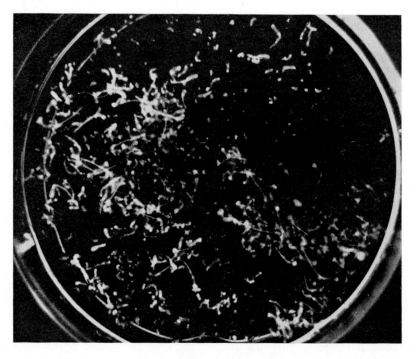

Fig. 7.3. Embryoids from cultured isolated pollen of *Nicotiana tabacum* after 21 days culture in synthetic medium.

inositol, 800 mg l^{-1} glutamine, and 100 mg l^{-1} *l*-serine. The technique shows great promise for the future and is now being applied to other genera.

7.5. *Factors affecting the growth of microspores* in vitro

7.5.1. *Stage of microspore development*

In order to induce growth of microspores when cultured either within an anther or after isolation, it is essential that the pollen be in a particular developmental stage. It was stated earlier that Nitsch was able to induce embryoid formation from microspores in cultured tobacco anthers by selecting anthers from flower buds in which the petals were approximately the same length as the sepals. The reason for this is that such anthers contained microspores at the critical stage when they can be induced to bypass their normal growth pattern. During normal development, the tetrads of spores formed at meiosis give rise to unicellular microspores. The nucleus of each microspore then undergoes replication of deoxyribonucleic acid followed by the first mitosis. The division is asymmetric and results in the formation of a large vegetative cell and a smaller generative cell. The generative nucleus divides again to produce two gametes, but normally the vegetative nucleus never divides again. Nitsch's group demonstrated that anthers containing microspores at the tetrad stage, or anthers containing almost mature pollen, failed to give rise to plantlets; they were formed only from microspores intermediate between these two stages of development.

N. Sunderland has examined the morphology of developing multicellular structures in *Nicotiana* species, as a result of which he suggests that there are two main types of development. In the first type, the microspore undergoes its first mitosis to form a vegetative and a generative cell. Subsequently, the generative nucleus undergoes no further division, or may undergo only a limited number of divisions. In this case the bulk of the multicellular structure is derived from derivatives of the vegetative nucleus. In the second type of development, both the generative and vegetative cell nuclei can undergo further divisions and contribute to the developing mass. It is also possible that the first microspore mitosis can be symmetric, producing two equal-sized nuclei both of which contribute to the developing mass. This has been observed in *Atropa, Datura, Nicotiana, Secale* and several other genera. Some of the different types of multicellular structures observed in *Secale* microspore cultures are shown in fig. 7.4. In the wheat-rye hybrid (*Triticale*) the first microspore mitosis produces two morphologically identical nuclei, but one of these always behaves in the manner of a generative nucleus. This generative-type nucleus can undergo numerous divisions without wall

125

formation, but eventually the vegetative nucleus divides and the cellular products of these divisions push the generative derivatives to the side of the microspore. When the wall of the microspore ruptures to release the multicellular structure, the generative derivatives are also released and disintegrate in the anther sac.

An explanation is required for the morphological diversity observed in the examples described. Such an explanation might result in the successful culture of microspores of other species, and in techniques being devised to increase the percentage of microspores undergoing development in culture. The studies of C. Nitsch and her co-workers suggest that microspores cultured during the first mitotic division

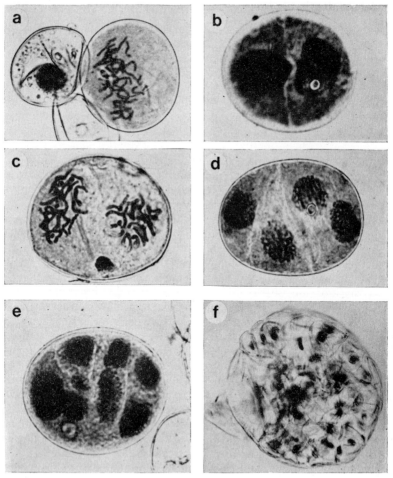

Fig. 7.4.

126

are most likely to undergo multicellular grain formation. This is also true for some species such as *Datura* and *Secale*. Nitsch's group provides evidence indicating that thermal shocks applied to microspores during mitosis can result in an alteration of the axis of mitosis and to an increase in the percentage of microspore embryogenesis. In some genera in which culture is successful, there is evidence suggesting that microspores can undergo development at the tetrad stage, e.g. *Pelargonium*, or at a stage immediately prior to germination, e.g. *Brassica oleracea*. In these cases the possibility that the second meiotic division or the second microspore mitosis are also stages susceptible to the stimulus of multicellular structure formation must not be ruled out.

It will be important in further studies in this field to subject developing anthers to treatments which might increase division in microspores, and to determine whether this increase results in a higher frequency of formation of multicellular structures. There have been reports that ethrel, a compound which releases the volatile growth regulator ethylene, can cause abnormal divisions in *Triticum* pollen, and that this pollen will give rise to multinuclear structures in culture. Ethrel also increases the number of multicellular structures in rice (*Oryza sativa*). The application of various growth regulators, of different temperatures, or of other environmental stimuli to plants before anther excision may radically alter the response of pollen during subsequent culture.

Fig. 7.4. The formation of multicellular microspores in cultured anthers of *Secale cereale*. All structures were observed in anthers cultured on Nitsch and Nitsch medium (Appendix Table 6) containing 2,4-D. Stained with acetocarmine. (*a*) Unicellular microspores prior to, and during, mitosis. They are present within the same anthers as the structures shown in (*b*), (*c*), and (*d*). Mitosis in one of the microspores is non-haploid ($n = 7$). This may be indicative of endomitosis or nuclear fusion in a free, haploid microspore, or it may represent an unreduced microspore undergoing development. (*b*) The first mitotic division has resulted in the formation of two equal-sized vegetative-type cells. (*c*) In this spore the first mitosis produced a small densely staining generative nucleus, and a larger more diffusely staining vegetative nucleus. The latter has undergone further divisions. Nuclei show the triploid chromosome number ($3n = 21$), which might suggest that nuclear fusion has followed a period of free division in the vegetative nucleus. (*d*) A microspore containing four equal-sized nuclei indicating its origin from a spore similar to the one in (*b*). (*e*) Multicellular spores containing densely staining embryoid-type cells. (*f*) Multicellular spore containing cells showing a high degree of vacuolation. Such spores are likely to form calluses.

127

7.5.2. Miscellaneous factors controlling microspore growth

In addition to the stage of pollen development and the incubation conditions already described, other factors control microspore growth in culture. Microspores within anthers from one flower bud may give a growth response, but microspores from another flower bud in exactly the same stage of development may fail to grow under identical cultural conditions. There is also evidence that when a succession of flowers is produced, the anthers from first-formed buds may contain microspores more responsive to culture than anthers from later-formed buds. Another phenomenon of frequent occurrence is that the microspores initially develop in culture into multicellular structures, but many of these later abort. The reason for this is unclear, but it may in part be due to unsuitable culture conditions, e.g. inadequate culture medium, or to competition between multicellular structures for compounds essential to their further development. It is possible that certain microspores may contain imbalanced chromosome numbers or lethal gene combinations which affect their subsequent growth in culture. As a consequence of these problems it is often necessary to set up large and extremely tedious screening procedures involving numerous variables before the microspores can be induced to give the desired response in culture.

7.6. Ploidy levels of anther-derived plantlets

Some of the plantlets developed from cultured anthers have been shown to be haploid, which confirms their origin from microspores. Such haploid plantlets can be diploidized by colchicine to give homozygous diploid individuals. Other plantlets derived from cultured anthers may possess ploidy levels varying from diploid to octaploid, and this leads to difficulties in explaining their origin. In a recent article, K. C. Engevild lists some possible mechanisms that could explain the formation of the various ploidy levels when the parent plant from which the anthers are excised is heterozygous. Because of the importance of this technique for practical plant breeding, these possibilities are also listed below:

(a) Endomitosis, in which stages of mitosis occur within the intact nuclear membrane leading to chromosome doubling, within haploid microspores. Result $2n$, $4n$, $8n$, etc. homozygotes. The same result would be achieved by endoreduplication, which involves chromosomal reproduction during interphase and is made manifest, for example, by the presence of diplochromosomes (4-chromatid chromosomes).

(b) Nuclear fusion within haploid microspores. Result—$2n$, $3n$, $4n$, $5n$, etc. homozygotes.

(c) Development of dyads and incomplete tetrads. Result—plants heterozygous at certain loci because of cross-over before the first meiotic division.

(d) Growth of pollen mother cells or of unreduced microspores. Result—heterozygote.

(e) Development of tapetum cells, connective, or anther wall. Result—heterozygote.

(f) Development of callus tissue from haploid microspores. Result—homozygous but also mutations and chimaeras (genetically non-uniform).

Engevild writes " unfortunately, several mechanisms might operate simultaneously. One could for example easily visualise the formation of diploids (and triploids) by a mixture of endomitosis in the pollen, fusion of nuclei in the pollen and embryoid formation directly from different kinds of unreduced pollen grains. It is therefore necessary to explore the mechanisms both by cytology and by segregation ratios in progenies of the plantlets. For practical breeding purposes, however, it will normally be sufficient to demonstrate that almost all plantlets are homozygous ". In certain cases this may not be necessary. It may be possible to recognize plants

Fig. 7.5. Young plant of *Hyoscyamus niger* showing filiform leaves (left) and normal leaves (right).

129

Fig. 7.6. Plants with filiform leaves obtained from microspore cultures of a *Hyoscyamus niger* plant heterozygous for normal leaf form and for the recessive filiform marker. Upper left the plant is haploid, upper right diploid, lower left triploid, and lower right tetraploid. Their origin from reduced microspores cannot be doubted.

Fig. 7.7. Schematic summary of a combined microbial technique with conventional crossings for plant breeding. In circles are the number of chromosomes, e.g. 48 = amphidiploid *Nicotiana tabacum*; 24 = haploid *N. tabacum*. (*a*) Normal plant of *N. tabacum* with petiolated leaves. (*b*) Meiosis in the anther. (*c*) Embryoids (haploid) in the anther. (*d*) Haploid plantlet from anther. (*e*) Haploid plant. (*f*) Section through a leaf. (*g*) Isolated mesophyll cells. (*h*) Protoplasts from mesophyll cells. (*i*) Petri dish with protoplasts; mutagenesis at this stage or in the leaves before preparation of the protoplasts; agar medium with selecting material, e.g. a plant parasite toxin. (*j*) and (*k*) Only a few resistant colonies growing. (*l*) Regenerating plants. (*m*) and (*n*) Rooted plants diploidized with colchicine. (*o*) Amphidiploid mutant (in this case with the recessive gene for petiole winged leaves) should be tested for resistance to the toxin.

derived from microspores through the use of genetic markers. As an illustration we can refer to the studies of G. Melchers with *Hyoscyamus niger* (henbane). In this plant normal leaf shape (N) is dominant to filiform leaf shape (n) (fig. 7.5). Thus, a heterozygote will always possess normal leaf form (Nn), and plantlets produced

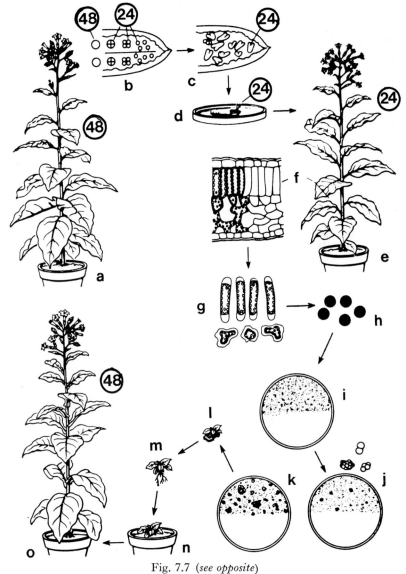

Fig. 7.7 (*see opposite*)

from cells other than microspores, of the heterozygote will be morphologically similar to the parent. Only when the alleles are separated during meiosis can the character for filiform leaf shape be expressed. The filiform plants shown in fig. 7. 6 were obtained from anther cultures of a heterozygote. It can therefore be stated with certainty without chromosome counts that these plants are derived from microspores.

7.7. *Application of haploid techniques to plant breeding*

G. Melchers realized almost 20 years ago that haploid cell cultures might be important to plant breeders. In a recent article he provides a very lucid account of the techniques now available. It should be possible to induce mutagenesis in meristems or in leaves of haploid plants and then from these to isolate protoplasts or single cells. If these are subsequently plated on to selective media containing antibiotics, amino acid analogues, fungal and bacterial toxins, or on to media with increased osmotic pressures, it should be possible to select new resistant genotypes (fig. 7.7). Such plants could then be incorporated into breeding programmes. Experiments such as those outlined above could be carried out on one single haploid plant. In species where large numbers of haploid plants can be produced from microspores, it is also possible that mutants could be obtained directly by subjecting unicellular microspores to mutagenic treatments before culture.

Even without mutation techniques, haploid production via the culture of microspores and macrospores, if properly utilized, should contribute to plant breeding. Its value lies in the speed with which homozygous plants can be obtained compared with conventional techniques of inbreeding; in many plants which are self-sterile haploid production, followed by diploidization, may be the only way of achieving homozygosity. As Melchers rightly indicates " the objection that today one does not strive to obtain homozygous material because heterozygotes may be more vigorous, is far too short-sighted to be taken in earnest by plant breeders; the possibility of obtaining exactly reproducible hybrid seeds again and again from truly homozygous starting lines is rather an interesting advantage for the breeder ". The production of haploid plants in large numbers from microspores could greatly facilitate plant breeding programmes that require a combination of dominant alleles. Let us assume, for example, that a particular variety carries a gene A which confers resistance to a particular fungal disease, and that another variety of the same species contains the gene B which confers resistance to other strains of the same fungus. Assume also that the breeder would prefer to have a plant resistant to all strains of the disease, i.e. one that is AABB. His procedure would be to cross-fertilize the two varieties, to grow up the F_1 hybrid seed, and then to self-fertilize the resulting plants. The procedure can be formulated thus:

AAbb × aaBB *parents*

AaBb F_1 *hybrid*

Microspores	AB	aB	Ab	ab	egg cells
AB	AABB	AaBB	AABb	AaBb	
aB	AaBB	aaBB	AaBb	aaBb	
Ab	AABb	AaBb	AAbb	Aabb	
ab	AaBb	aaBb	Aabb	aabb	

Theoretically, one-quarter of the microspores contain the combination AB, and by doubling the chromosome complements the double dominant AABB is obtained. There is no problem in recognizing the double dominant genotype, because all others will be resistant only to one of the fungal diseases or will not be resistant to any (combinations aaBB, AAbb and aabb), and they can immediately be discarded. Examination of the table shows that the breeder has produced large numbers of different genotypes, of which only one-sixteenth has the desired combination. However, he is unable to distinguish this combination from the heterozygotes which are phenotypically similar (AaBB, AABb and AaBb). Consequently, he must again inbreed before the double dominant character can be recognized with certainty. Another advantage to breeders, which will be within reach when large numbers of microspores can be successfully cultured, is the possibility of uncovering new and highly beneficial gene combinations. If one of the parents of the F_1 hybrid also possesses high-yielding qualities, it should be possible to combine these qualities with double disease resistance. It is likely that some microspores in the anther of an F_1 hybrid will therefore contain superior gene combinations to either of the parents. If such microspores can be induced to form plantlets in culture, these plants will immediately be suitable for commerical release.

Scientists at the Iwata tobacco institute in Japan have been attempting to improve the character of tobacco cultivars by introducing genes for resistance to wilt disease, for more tolerance to drying up of leaves, and for higher productivity. They crossed varieties containing the required characters with their commercial lines, and subjected the F_1 progeny to anther culture. Their cultures produced 150 microspore plants, and of these, six showing the desired characters were selected for further study. At the time of writing this book trials are being undertaken to determine the productivity and adaptability of the new plant types. The whole programme has taken just two years, whereas it would have taken six years to reach a similar result by conventional breeding techniques.

7.8. *Summary*

As long ago as 1959 it was pointed out that the availability of techniques for large-scale tissue production and plant regeneration from single haploid cells offered a new and important tool for plant breeding and genetics. At that time only small numbers of naturally occurring haploid plants were available. The techniques described in this chapter provide a way of obtaining large numbers of haploid or homozygous plants. The example of the work on tobacco by Japanese scientists demonstrates the potential of microspore culture techniques in plant breeding. These methods are now being applied to plants of more direct food value, and if these studies are successful plant tissue culture will have provided an important service to agriculture. More recent manipulations with haploid plant cells such as mutagenesis treatments and somatic cell hybridization will be discussed in Chapter 8, since they lay the foundation for future experimentation with plant cells along lines that have been so successful in the rapid development of microbial and molecular genetics.

CHAPTER 8
plant tissue culture—present and future

8.1. *Introduction*

THROUGHOUT this book we have described in historical sequence the major developments that have taken place in plant tissue culture, together with some of the applications which have stemmed from them. Within this field of study there still exist numerous problems which must be overcome if the full potential offered by plant tissue culture is to be realized. In this chapter some of these problems will be discussed in relation to future prospects. We have placed emphasis on the difficulties encountered with this technique, as we feel it necessary for the reader to make an objective assessment of this branch of plant science, and to develop a critical approach to his studies.

8.2. *Are all living cells totipotent?*

In recent years great progress has been made in inducing organ formation from cultured cells. Root formation occurs quite commonly in many tissues, and in some cultures, e.g. those of *Atropa*, *Daucus* and *Nicotiana* it is possible to initiate roots, or shoots, or embryoids, by altering the constituents of the culture medium. The evidence that cultures contain cells that are totipotent in the sense of being capable of forming embryo-like structures has led to the view that differentiation of cells *in vivo* does not involve loss or permanent inactivation of genetic material. This generalization clearly implies that all mature living cells in all whole plants can be induced to express their genetic information via embryogenesis on transfer to culture. The fact remains that many cultured tissues, although usually not reported, cannot be induced to express any kind of morphogenesis, and even in embryologically competent cultures only a very small proportion of the cells give rise to embryoids. W. Halperin has indicated that these structures may arise only from relatively simple parenchymatous cells which are carried over from the plant during callus initiation. Some cells in the intact plant may be highly specialized and incapable of division. Other cells from intact tissues, though capable of dividing and contributing to a callus, may retain certain differentiated functions which restrict their morphogenetic potential. This may be true of some polyploid cells. Indeed, there have been reports indicating that certain

135

differentiated functions of the explant can persist in callus cultures. The leaves of the English ivy (*Hedera helix*), for example, show a characteristic dimorphism. The juvenile form is a vine possessing lobed leaves, whereas the mature fruiting form is shrubby, upright, and possesses entire leaves. In 1965 Y. T. Stoutemeyer and O. K. Britt reported that under their cultural conditions calluses from the stems of the two growth phases of the same plant consistently behaved differently. The cultures from the juvenile stage possess a higher proliferation rate and larger cells, and these differences between the calluses persisted over a period of two years.

Observations on embryogenesis in cultured tissues have led to a proposed sequence of events in which single cells develop directly into globular or filamentous proembryos, but at the time of writing we are unaware of any critical data substantiating this claim. Anatomical studies do suggest that single cells within aggregates, or within certain tissues of plantlets derived from tissue cultures, e.g. epidermal cells of *Ranunculus*, can undergo embryogenesis directly. A similar situation exists in the development of specialized cell types such as phloem or xylem cells. Although these can often be observed in callus or suspension cultures, they are generally found within aggregates. An association of cells may therefore be necessary to provide the appropriate environment for certain individuals to express their totipotency. However, the very recent studies of Kohlenbach (see 6.2.3.) do provide an exception. Unicellular microspores of some plants have been observed to develop directly into embryoids. It may be possible to apply the knowledge gained from these cultures to induce a similar response in isolated somatic cells. When one examines a developing multicellular microspore in culture, or a single dividing epidermal cell of *Ranunculus*, both systems show a common feature; they undergo divisions within the existing cell. If it is possible to induce similar internal divisions in isolated vegetative cells, it may be possible to induce embryogenesis directly without an intervening callus phase. Possibly this aim may be achieved by plasmolysing an isolated cell and inducing the plasmolysed protoplast to regenerate a new wall within the existing cell wall (cf. exine and intine of a microspore). The original wall might then act as a barrier to free proliferation of cells, and restrict organized divisions to the internal regenerated cell, leading to embryogenesis. To achieve this aim may overcome many of the problems which occur when plant cells are first grown as calluses and cell suspensions. Some of these problems will be discussed later in this chapter.

The inability of certain cultures to respond to morphogenetic stimuli may be, in part, because the explant or cell used to initiate the cultures cannot be easily de-differentiated (or embryonized), or because the cultured cells are genetically non-totipotent. Alternatively, it may be related to difficulties encountered in applying the correct sequence of treatments. As an example of these difficulties we can refer to calluses of rye. Tissue cultures of cereals have always proved rather difficult to culture, and excised anthers of rye rapidly become necrotic on a medium containing auxin, cytokinin, and gibberellin. When placed on medium containing only auxin they give rise to actively growing calluses from the filament tissue. These calluses form large numbers of roots, but shoot formation is a rare event. However, when root-forming calluses are transferred to medium containing auxin, cytokinin, and gibberellin, the roots initiate a new callus which spontaneously forms large numbers of shoots. A possible cause of these effects is that the anther filament may contain different types and concentrations of growth hormones from those in the roots initiated on the filament-derived calluses. Identification of these hormones in individual plant species may assist further progress in morphogenesis. Another possible approach for species which do not respond to morphogenetic stimuli would be to obtain cultures from their meristems or from zygotic embryos. Studies by Steward and his co-workers have shown that cultures initiated from these sources possess a greater embryogenic ability than calluses from root or stem explants. Similarly, shoot-tip cultures of various genera within the Orchidaceae readily proliferate and give rise directly to large numbers of protocorms (embryoids). As Street indicates, the further cytodifferentiation progresses as plant development proceeds, the more difficult it may become to achieve the required ' de-differentiation '.

8.3. Cytological instability of cell cultures

A further advantage of using cells isolated from plant meristems to initiate cultures is that such cells are more likely to be of uniform ploidy. In general, cultures are obtained from complex explants of roots, stems, leaves, and other organs (Chapter 4). It is therefore not very surprising to find that the cells within the cultures are not only morphologically different, but show also various levels of polyploidy. Endopolyploidy is of frequent occurrence in the differentiated tissues of higher plants, which raises two questions of relevance. First, do the abnormalities observed in some cultured tissues result from a non-selective induction of growth of cells in the original heterogeneous explant? Second, if the cultures are derived from cells of known genetics, do the various ploidy levels indicate cytological instability in culture, or do they indicate that under certain conditions cultured plant cells are merely expressing their ability to undergo cellular differentiation? In a careful study of the nuclear behaviour and karyotypic evolution of cultures of *Crepis capillaris* (smooth hawk's beard), M. D. Sacristan showed that 78·5 per cent

K

of the sub-cultures maintained their original diploid level for more than a year. The problem of maintaining haploidy in haploid cultures was greater, but even with these 34·1 per cent of the sub-cultures retained their haploid number for a similar period of time. The results with these cultures are particularly significant, since it has been reported that *Crepis* is a plant in which cellular differentiation occurs without endopolyploidy. Thus, it appears that in this case the chromosomal abnormalities (aberrant karyotypes and polyploidy) which were observed in the cultured cells were not derived from the original explant; neither were they a feature of cellular differentiation occurring *in vitro*, but probably resulted from cytological instability in culture.

In cell cultures such as those of deadly nightshade, where morphogenesis can be readily induced in recently-initiated tissues, there occurs an apparent loss of ability to exhibit this response after prolonged maintenance by sub-culture. It has been suggested that cultures may lose their ability to synthezise specific organ-forming factors, or that non-mutational processes similar to those taking place during plant ageing could occur in culture and affect organ-forming ability. Genomic imbalance resulting from aneuploidy or high levels of polyploidy has also been suggested as a cause of loss of organogenetic ability. However, no evidence exists which convincingly correlates the two. In Chapter 7, for example, we discussed how plants varying from haploid to octaploid can be obtained from cultured microspores. Similarly, T. Murashige and R. Nakano found that aneuploidy was a typical feature of morphogenetically repressed cultures, but it may not always be equated with total loss of organ-forming capacity. Thus, the presence of aneuploidy resulted in different degrees of repression of root and shoot formation in the tobacco cultures. In these cases they consider that the degree to which organogenesis is repressed will depend upon the specific chromosomes and their numbers involved in the nuclear modification.

Important questions are posed by these findings. What is the cause of these chromosomal changes in cultured tissues, and can they be prevented? In cultures of pea J. G. Torrey showed that kinetin-free medium stimulates the development only of diploid cells present in the explant, whereas medium containing kinetin also encourages the development of polyploid cells. It is also unclear how far abnormal cells which may be present in the cultures can be prevented from undergoing further development. C. F. Demoise and C. R. Partanen observed a fluctuating population of diploid and tetraploid cell types in cultures of the garden peony (*Paeonia suffruticosa*). They suggested that under their cultural conditions the production of polyploid cells from diploid cells may occur, but that the polyploid cells had only a limited capacity for cell division, resulting in the reappearance of a largely diploid population. In his studies with carrot callus and cell suspensions, W. Halperin found that the suspension cultures retained their high morphogenetic capacity for long periods, whereas this capacity was soon lost in callus tissues. He observed also that the carrot calluses became entirely aneuploid, but the suspensions remained diploid. He assumed that under the comparatively harsh conditions which prevail in suspension culture, mitosis could only occur in the cell aggregate fraction that consisted predominately of diploid " proembryogenic masses ". In the callus, however, the intense conditioning effect of the tissue mass permitted the division of aneuploid cells to occur at the expense of the diploid cells. Thus, the experimental evidence indicates that in certain instances it may be possible to eliminate undesirable cellular geno-types from cultures by correct control of the physical and chemical environment of the cells.

We know virtually nothing of the effect of some of the newer cultural techniques on the cytological stability of cultured cells. Normally, cultures are allowed to grow for various time periods on a medium before being transferred to fresh medium. As a consequence, a culture may be a mixture of cells in various physiological, morphological, and differentiated states. A major advance towards overcoming this problem has been the development of continuous chemostat and turbidostat systems similar to those already used for growing micro-organisms. As yet, the techniques have been applied to only a few species. This is because most cell suspensions are highly aggregated, which hampers attempts to culture them in such refined vessels. Addition of cell-separating enzymes at low concentrations to culture media may help to reduce the size of cell clumps in suspensions. It remains to be seen whether fermenter-type culture systems will be useful for obtaining uniform populations of dividing cells, which can be induced to show the desired morphogenetic response.

Most callus and suspension cultures are obtained indirectly by inducing the growth of cells in large explants. They are referred to as secondary cultures. Mechanical and enzymatic methods are now in use which enable very large numbers of single cells or protoplasts to be isolated directly from plant organs. These cells in nutrient media are termed primary cultures. Very little is known of the extent to which the behaviour of cells in primary cultures can be controlled by adjusting their physical and chemical environments, or of the uniformity of such cultures. It should therefore be a feature of further studies to attempt to obtain a population of single cells directly from plant meristems, to determine their uniformity in response to morphogenetic compounds, and to compare this response with the response of more highly differentiated cells.

Halperin has expressed doubt of the feasibility of obtaining uniform populations of cells directly from plant meristems, as he considers such populations may be a mixture of cells which are the "functional equivalent of different kinds of blast cells" in animals. Studies with blast cells indicate that they are committed to a set pattern of differentiation.

Plant protoplast techniques may provide a means of obtaining a uniform population of single cells. It may be possible to isolate a mutant protoplast, which, under certain conditions (e.g. elevated temperature) fails to produce a cell wall but which still divides to give a population of synchronously dividing, non-aggregating protoplasts. Alteration of the cultural conditions might then induce such protoplasts to regenerate new cell walls and to undergo the desired morphogenetic response. That such an aim may not be too futuristic is suggested by the work of G. Melchers and L. Bergmann in 1958 with a haploid callus culture of snapdragon. After X-ray treatment of the tissue, a variant was obtained in which the cells were only loosely aggregated, and from these studies Melchers has emphasized the importance of obtaining temperature-sensitive mutants, especially those for pectin synthesis, for further study. If a uniform population of cells can be obtained and the cells within this population converted *en masse* to roots, shoots, embryoids, or to specialized cell types, then an ideal system will have been established. In spite of the problems in obtaining such an ideal, cultures do exist in which these responses can be accomplished. Those of tobacco are the best-known model systems, closely followed by cultures of nightshade and carrot. It is likely that in the near future the number of species in which these responses can be induced will increase, and studies with these species may lead to a perfection of techniques which can be more widely applied to economically important plants.

The genetic variation and genetic instability encountered in cultures are undesirable for most scientific studies and for the preservation and propagation of rare or valuable genotypes. Recently, methods have been developed for preserving plant cells at very low temperatures over long periods. Carrot cultures have been deep frozen in the presence of protective agents, and actively growing cultures capable of embryogenesis re-established after thawing. Such methods may be employed to preserve potentially useful cells before they undergo detrimental genotypic changes in culture. Freezing techniques may also result in the establishment of tissue banks of specific cell lines which could be re-established when required. The genetic variation encountered in cell cultures might however, be harnessed or even increased to provide a wider variation of genotypes suitable for incorporation into plant breeding programmes. In the final part of this chapter we shall describe some of the attempts to achieve this aim. Interpretation of many of the studies must be treated with caution since it is a comparatively new field in which very little is known.

8.4. Mutant cell lines

Mutant strains of micro-organisms have contributed much to biochemical and genetical studies, and mutant cell lines would be of similar importance in studies of higher plants. After the finding that haploid tissue could be obtained from cultured microspores, efforts have been made to obtain mutants from such tissue. One of the problems facing research on cell mutation is the difficulty of selecting the mutated cells out of the rest of the culture. P. S. Carlson, using a selection system modelled on one previously used for cultured animal cells, reported obtaining, from haploid cells of tobacco, mutants that were auxotrophic. These, also referred to as nutritional or biochemical mutants, are unable to synthesize a particular compound such as an amino acid or vitamin. Consequently, unlike the normal or wild-type cells which can grow on minimal or unsupplemented medium, they must be supplied with the specific compound or compounds that they are unable to synthesize. In the technique used by Carlson, a mixed population of auxotrophic and wild-type cells is placed in an unsupplemented medium which allows the wild-type cells to divide, but which prevents division in the auxotrophs. The cells are then exposed to a compound which kills only dividing cells. After filtrates of single cells and small cell aggregates had been exposed to the action of the mutagen ethyl methane-sulphonate (EMS) and allowed to begin dividing in an unsupplemented medium, they were exposed to 5-bromodeoxyuridine (BUdR). Growing cells incorporated this into their deoxyribonucleic acid, and were subsequently killed on exposure to light. The surviving ' auxotrophic ' cells were then recovered by culturing them on medium containing nutritional supplements including casein hydrolysate, yeast extract, and thymidine, which permitted their growth into calluses. Portions of these calluses were then tested to determine more specifically their nutritional requirements. In this manner Carlson reported obtaining cell colonies auxotrophic for p-aminobenzoic acid, arginine, biotin, hypoxanthine, proline, and lysine. However, the study was not without its problems, for all the cell colonies were reported to grow, if only slowly, on unsupplemented medium. Carlson suggests that one of the possible reasons for the observations is that as *Nicotiana tabacum* is an allopolyploid, the so-called ' haploid ' cells may contain two physiologically different copies of the metabolically important genes. The results suggest that it would be far simpler to work with true haploid plants which contain single gene copies.

141

In the previous chapter brief mention was made of the possibility of obtaining plants resistant to the harmful effects of microbial toxins. In 1969 H. Binding, K. Binding and J. Straub succeeded in obtaining streptomycin-resistant calluses from haploid cultures of *Petunia hybrida*, and in 1973 P. Maliga, A. SZ-Brenovits and L. Márton reported the production of streptomycin-resistant plants from callus cultures of haploid tobacco. Carlson has also obtained tobacco cell mutants resistant to the methionine analogue, methionine sulphoximine, a compound structurally similar to the toxin produced by the pathogenic bacterium *Pseudomonas tabaci* responsible for wildfire disease of tobacco. Plants regenerated from the cells resistant to methionine sulphoximine exhibited a greater resistance to wildfire disease after inoculation with the pathogen than did normal control plants.

One of the problems of using presumed ' haploid ' calluses and cell suspension cultures for mutagenesis is that the cultures undergo spontaneous chromosome doubling. In addition, there is no guarantee that the explant obtained from the haploid donor plant is entirely haploid. It is possible that, during cytodifferentiation, originally haploid cells in the meristems (which are the only parts of the plant normally tested for ploidy level) undergo chromosome duplication giving rise to diploid cells or successive reduplications giving cells of higher ploidy level. One way to overcome this problem would be to attempt to mutate haploid microspores in the unicellular stage, and to regenerate plantlets directly from the microspores. M. Devreux and his colleagues recently reported the results of studies with irradiated tobacco microspores. Earlier studies had shown that numerous aberrant plant types could be distinguished amongst the products of the irradiated microspores. However, they found it difficult to distinguish between mutant plants, and plants arising from naturally occurring recombinants. They have overcome this problem very simply by subjecting microspores from homozygous plants (themselves derived from anther culture) to mutagenesis. In such a case any modified microspore plantlet which may be obtained cannot be ascribed to genetic recombinations, and should be the result of mutation. Such techniques are extremely attractive in those species in which it is easy to produce large numbers of plantlets directly from microspores, since they are rapid and avoid the necessity of going through a callus phase. Unfortunately, for many economically important plants success in microspore culture is very limited. In these cases advantage must be taken of the few haploid plants that exist. The organs of such plants or single cells or protoplasts isolated directly from these organs should be subjected to mutagenic treatments, and the cells should be grown under conditions that select for aberrant phenotypes. Such mutagenic techniques may result in advances in cell physiology, biochemistry, genetics, and plant breeding (Chapter 7).

8.5. *Modification of plant cells*

Isolated protoplasts devoid of cell walls provide an experimental system for attempting to introduce foreign materials into the cytoplasm of plant cells. Indeed, there are already reports of the uptake of inert particles, macromolecules, organelles, and micro-organisms into protoplasts. With such a system it may be possible to attempt to modify existing plant cells to perform specific functions. An example of such modification would be the genetic alteration of cells of non-leguminous plants to enable them to form an association with *Rhizobium*, a soil bacterium normally responsible for fixing atmospheric nitrogen in cells of root nodules of legumes such as pea, bean, clover, soybean, and cowpea. Modified plants, e.g. cereals capable of fixing their own nitrogen, may be important in economically backward areas where the cost of nitrate fertilizers is inhibitive. Cell modification may perhaps be achieved by uptake of nitrogen fixing bacteria, by the uptake and expression of genetic material controlling nitrogen fixation in free-living micro-organisms, or by transfer of genetic material controlling the nitrogen-fixing association with *Rhizobium* from legumes to non-legumes by somatic hybridization of isolated protoplasts (Chapter 5).

The success of these aims depends upon the ability to isolate viable protoplasts, to accomplish the desired modification, to select preferentially the modified cells in the cultures, and to grow them into calluses from which whole plants can be regenerated. Plant protoplasts are by no means easy to culture, and even the most experienced worker faces difficulties in obtaining viable preparations. In Chapter 5 we described some of the events occurring in isolated protoplasts after the naked cells are stimulated into cytoplasmic activity on transfer to suitable culture media. Wall regeneration is not necessarily followed by division. The latter demands the stimulation of intense metabolic activity with synthesis of new cytoplasm. As yet, only a limited number of protoplast systems are capable of sustained division to produce cell colonies. The number from which whole plants can be regenerated is even more restricted. These problems point to our lack of knowledge of the fundamental requirements of isolated protoplasts and cells in culture. They may indicate a need to improve culture media and techniques, and to control more stringently the environment of the donor plants before protoplasts of other species can be isolated and grown.

As protoplasts first develop into cell colonies in culture, the technique faces all the problems inherent in growing callus tissues,

143

such as changes in chromosome number during culture. In some laboratories protoplasts are cultured in liquid media, which allows the naked cells to adhere and aggregate; callus tissues may therefore develop from more than one cell. Genetic variation in these cells will produce heterogeneous calluses, which may result in the development of chimaeras. This emphasizes the need to culture protoplasts as freely dispersed individuals, and to use nurse tissue, conditioned media, or feeder layers to reduce the inoculum density to a minimum. Low density inocula are of the utmost importance in attempting to isolate experimentally modified plant cells, whether they are cells or protoplasts which have been subjected to mutagenic treatment, or protoplasts subjected to uptake and fusion treatments. It is at this stage of plating in agar that the greatest difficulty is experienced in devising a selection system powerful enough to select cells of interest, since the modification event will occur at the very low frequency of a few cells in several millions. In combination with selective media, low density inocula greatly assist in retrieving genetically modified cells from the rest of the population. It now remains to be seen whether or not macromolecules such as bacterial deoxyribonucleic acid can be expressed in higher plant cells.

At the time of writing this book there are two reports on the production of hybrid plants by protoplast fusion. P. S. Carlson, H. H. Smith and R. D. Dearing reported obtaining a hybrid between *Nicotiana glauca* and *N. langsdorffii*. In nature these species are sexually compatible, and when crossed produce a hybrid carrying genetic characteristics for the development of tumours. As discussed in Chapter 4, cells from tumours can normally be grown on hormone-free media, whereas cells from normal tissues generally require a supply of exogenous hormones for growth. Carlson and his colleagues had the idea of using this property of tumorous tissues as a selection method for fused hybrid protoplasts of the two species. However, this intended selection method was not, in fact, employed. Their actual procedure, which is often wrongly reported, was to subject protoplasts of the two species to fusion treatment, and then to plate the mixture of fused and unfused protoplasts in a medium containing auxin and kinetin. They obtained 33 calluses which were only *later* transferred to medium lacking hormones. Here the tissues continued active growth. The possibility therefore existed that the calluses were mutants or habituations to hormone autotrophy, rather than developing from fusion products. Shoots regenerated from three of the calluses were maintained by grafting on to young stem stocks of *N. glauca*. In spite of the fact that hormone-free media were not used to select the original fused hybrid protoplasts, these regenerated shoots were identical to shoots of the sexually produced hybrid. The idea of using such a selection system is good, but conditions

144

Fig. 8.1. (a) Demonstration of the light sensitivity and chlorophyll deficiency of two *Nicotiana tabacum* varieties, v (far right) and s (far left), and of the complementation for normal growth and chlorophyll in the sexually produced hybrids (v × s and s × v). (b) A dark green colony (arrowed) derived from fusion of protoplasts from the two varieties v and s. Other colonies on the plate are greenish-yellow in colour, and have developed from unfused protoplasts of the two varieties. (c) Sexual hybrid (v × s, left) and somatic hybrid (v + s, right). Morphologically both are very similar.

145

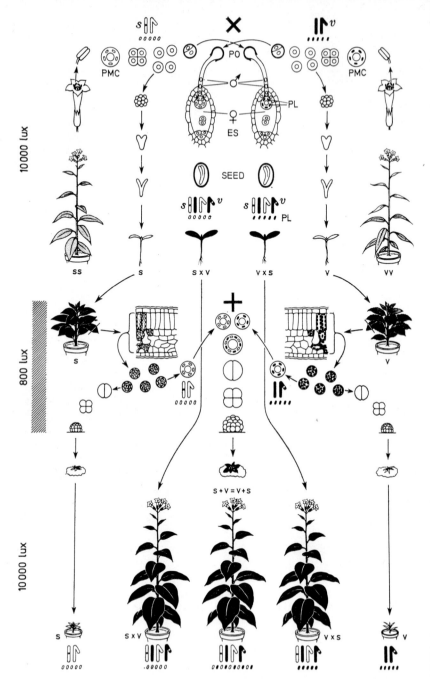

Fig. 8.2. Diagram illustrating normal sexual hybrid production (s × v or v × s) and somatic hybridization (s + v = v + s), from two light sensitive, chlorophyll deficient varieties v and s of *Nicotiana tabacum*. PMC pollen mother cell, PO pollen with tube, ES embryo sac, PL plastids.

should be determined which permit hybrid protoplasts to grow and regenerate on hormone-free media.

The most recent report of production of hybrids from protoplasts comes from G. Melchers and W. Keller. The selection system used in their experiment is extremely interesting, and may be applicable to fusion hybrids of other species. They used two different varieties of *Nicotiana tabacum*, both of which were chlorophyll deficient and light sensitive. However, the sexually produced hybrids expressed complementation for normal chlorophyll content, and were not light sensitive (fig. 8.1 *a*). Haploids of the parental varieties were produced by microspore culture methods, and were maintained under low intensity light. Protoplasts from the haploids were mixed, fused in a solution of 0·05 M calcium chloride and 0·4 M mannitol in glycine–sodium hydroxide buffer of pH 10·5 at 37°C, and the mixture of fused and unfused protoplasts plated. During the first 48 hours the protoplasts were incubated under a light intensity of 300 lux, which was subsequently increased to 3000 lux. After two to three weeks the cultures forming calluses were diluted and grown under a light intensity of 8000 to 10 000 lux. Most of the calluses were light greenish-yellow in colour. Others were very dark green (fig. 8.1 *b*)., and from some of these dark green colonies plantlets were regenerated which were identical to the sexually produced hybrid (fig. 8.1 *c*). So far, 11 hybrid plants derived from different fusion bodies have been produced, the first of which has been grown to flowering and the seed progeny germinated. The latter consisted of the same green, yellow, and whitish seedlings as are normally produced on germination of seeds from the sexual hybrid. The experiment is summarized diagramatically in fig. 8.2. Under light of 10 000 lux the parental types (ss and vv) are pale green. However, they can be induced to flower and can be cross-fertilized by conventional means (X). The resulting seeds give rise to seedlings which under light of 10 000 lux are green (s × v, v × s). For somatic hybridization (+) of the two parental types, anthers are cultured and induced to produce haploid microspore plantlets (s or v). Unlike the sexually produced seedlings, the microspore plantlets under light of 10 000 lux are pale green. However, if they are transferred to light of 800 lux they become green and can be used as a source of leaf mesophyll protoplasts. The isolated protoplasts can be fused, plated, and induced to form small callus colonies. The latter can be gradually transferred to light of 10 000 lux and induced to regenerate plantlets. Only fusion hybrids (s + v or v + s) give rise to green plants (s + v or v + s). Colonies arising from unfused protoplasts give rise to pale green plantlets (s or v). The experiment is a convincing demonstration of the potential offered by plant protoplast techniques. Efforts are now being made in many laboratories to obtain hybrids from economically important crop plants. The possibility exists that some hybridizations will be achieved which are not possible by cross pollination, but because of genetic incompatibility this range may be limited.

8.6. *Conclusion*

In this chapter our emphasis on problems is deliberate because we feel there is a necessity to develop new ideas, new techniques, and new approaches to overcome them. In spite of these difficulties, the development of methods for growing plant cells in continuous culture, the availability of haploid cells, techniques of single-cell cloning, mutation, and mutant selection, for the first time make possible advances in the cellular physiology of higher plants comparable to those already achieved with micro-organisms. The application of microbiological methods to plant cells is so new and the numbers of research papers on this subject are so limited at the present time, that any reports should be critically evaluated to assess whether or not they make a significant contribution to progress in this field. We have also seen in the previous chapters how culture methods are already being used to propagate and improve the quality and yield of commercially important plants. As the techniques are perfected they will be applied to a wider range of species, and consequently they should occupy a new role in plant breeding programmes.

G. Haberlandt first put forward his postulates over half a century ago. Since then, many scientists from all over the world have played their parts in accumulating knowledge which has now enabled isolated cells to be grown under carefully controlled experimental conditions through to whole plants. The technique of plant tissue culture is now being used to solve many very fundamental and applied problems in botany, but several years may elapse before cultured cells are exploited to their full potential. Many technical obstacles are associated with the handling of complex living systems. Some of these have been overcome, but many will surely remain for future generations of biologists.

APPENDIX

Table 1. A basal root culture medium. (After P. R. White as modified in the laboratory of H. E. Street.)

	Constituent		Concentration (mg litre^{-1} medium)
(1)	Calcium nitrate	$Ca(NO_3)_2 4H_2O$	288
(2)	Magnesium sulphate	$MgSO_4 7H_2O$	370
(3)	Potassium chloride	KCl	65
(4)	Potassium nitrate	KNO_3	80
(5)	Sodium dihydrogen phosphate	$NaH_2PO_4 4H_2O$	21·5
(6)	Sodium sulphate	$Na_2SO_4 10H_2O$	226·7
(7)	Boric acid	H_3BO_3	1·5
(8)	Copper sulphate	$CuSO_4 5H_2O$	0·02
(9)	Manganese chloride	$MnCl_2 4H_2O$	6·0
(10)	Molybdic acid	H_2MoO_4	0·0017
(11)	Potassium iodide	KI	0·75
(12)	Zinc sulphate	$ZnSO_4 7H_2O$	2·65
(13)	Ferric ethylenediamine tetra-acetate	FeEDTA	7·84*
(14)	Glycine		3·0
(15)	Nicotinic acid		0·5
(16)	Pyridoxine hydrochloride		0·1
(17)	Thiamine hydrochloride		0·1
(18)	Sucrose		15 000
	pH 4·9		

*FeEDTA solution is prepared by dissolving 0·74 g Na_2EDTA and 0·324 g $FeCl_3$ in 100 ml water.   1 ml is added per litre medium.

Table 2. Medium for *Atropa belladonna* callus and cell suspension cultures. (After P. R. White with inorganic supplements and growth substances of H. N. Wood and A. C. Braun.)

Constituent		Concentration (mg litre^{-1} medium)
(1) Ammonium sulphate	$(NH_4)_2SO_4$	790
(2) Calcium nitrate	$Ca(NO_3)_24H_2O$	288
(3) Magnesium sulphate	$MgSO_47H_2O$	1738
(4) Potassium chloride	KCl	910
(5) Sodium dihydrogen phosphate	$NaH_2PO_47H_2O$	388
(6) Sodium nitrate	$NaNO_3$	1800
(7) Sodium sulphate	$Na_2SO_410H_2O$	458
(8) Boric acid	H_3BO_3	1·5
(9) Manganese sulphate	$MnSO_44H_2O$	6·6
(10) Potassium iodide	KI	0·75
(11) Zinc sulphate	$ZnSO_47H_2O$	2·7
(12) Ferric ethylenediamine tetra-acetate	FeEDTA	7·84
(13) Glycine		3·0
(14) Meso-inositol		100
(15) Nicotinic acid		0·5
(16) Pyridoxine hydrochloride		0·1
(17) Thiamine hydrochloride		0·1
(18) NAA		2·0
(19) Kinetin		0·5 (callus)
		0·1 (suspension)
(20) Sucrose		20 000
pH 5·2		

For callus add 0·6 per cent w/v agar.

Table 3. Medium for *Acer pseudoplatanus* suspension cells. (After R. Heller
as modified in the laboratory of H. E. Street.)

	Constituent		Concentration (mg litre $^{-1}$ medium)
(1)	Calcium chloride	$CaCl_2 6H_2O$	111·7
(2)	Magnesium sulphate	$MgSO_4 7H_2O$	250
(3)	Potassium chloride	KCl	750
(4)	Sodium dihydrogen phosphate	$NaH_2PO_4 2H_2O$	150
(5)	Sodium nitrate	$NaNO_3$	600
(6)	Boric acid	H_3BO_3	1·0
(7)	Copper sulphate	$CuSO_4 5H_2O$	0·03
(8)	Manganese sulphate	$MnSO_4 4H_2O$	0·1
(9)	Potassium iodide	KI	0·01
(10)	Zinc sulphate	$ZnSO_4 7H_2O$	1·0
(11)	Ferric chloride	$FeCl_3 6H_2O$	1·0
(12)	Urea		200
(13)	Choline chloride		0·5
(14)	Cysteine hydrochloride		10·0
(15)	Meso-inositol		100
(16)	Pantothenic acid		2·5
(17)	Thiamine hydrochloride		1·0
(18)	2,4-D		1·0
(19)	Kinetin		0·25
(20)	Sucrose		20 000
	pH 5·2		

For *Acer* callus, ferric chloride is replaced by FeEDTA (2×10^{-2} M), and cysteine hydrochloride, choline chloride, meso-inositol, pantothenic acid, and kinetin are replaced by 10 per cent v/v autoclaved coconut milk. Agar is added at 0·6 per cent w/v.

Table 4. Medium for *Allium cepa* callus. (After O. L. Gamborg, R. A. Miller, and K. Ojima).

	Constituent		Concentration (mg litre^{-1} medium)
(1)	Ammonium sulphate	$(NH_4)_2SO_4$	134
(2)	Calcium chloride	$CaCl_2 2H_2O$	150
(3)	Magnesium sulphate	$MgSO_4 7H_2O$	250
(4)	Potassium nitrate	KNO_3	2500
(5)	Sodium dihydrogen phosphate	$NaH_2PO_4 2H_2O$	150
(6)	Boric acid	H_3BO_3	3·0
(7)	Cobalt chloride	$CoCl_2 6H_2O$	0·025
(8)	Copper sulphate	$CuSO_4 5H_2O$	0·025
(9)	Manganese sulphate	$MnSO_4 4H_2O$	10·0
(10)	Potassium iodide	KI	0·75
(11)	Sodium molybdate	$Na_2MoO_4 2H_2O$	0·25
(12)	Zinc sulphate	$ZnSO_4 7H_2O$	2·0
(13)	Sequestrene 330 iron		28·0
(14)	Meso-inositol		100
(15)	Nicotinic acid		1·0
(16)	Pyridoxine hydrochloride		1·0
(17)	Thiamine hydrochloride		1·0
(18)	2,4-D		1·0
(19)	Sucrose		20 000

pH 5·8

Agar 0·6 per cent w/v

Table 5. Medium for *Nicotiana tabacum* stem callus. (After T. Murashige and F. Skoog).

	Constituent		Concentration (mg litre^{-1} medium)
(1)	Ammonium nitrate	NH_4NO_3	1650
(2)	Calcium chloride	$CaCl_22H_2O$	440
(3)	Magnesium sulphate	$MgSO_47H_2O$	370
(4)	Potassium dihydrogen phosphate	KH_2PO_4	170
(5)	Potassium nitrate	KNO_3	1900
(6)	Boric acid	H_3BO_3	6·2
(7)	Cobalt chloride	$CoCl_26H_2O$	0·025
(8)	Copper sulphate	$CuSO_45H_2O$	0·025
(9)	Manganese sulphate	$MnSO_44H_2O$	22·3
(10)	Potassium iodide	KI	0·83
(11)	Sodium molybdate	$Na_2MoO_42H_2O$	0·25
(12)	Zinc sulphate	$ZnSO_44H_2O$	8·6
(13)	Disodium ethylenediamine tetra-acetate	Na_2EDTA	37·3
(14)	Ferrous sulphate	$FeSO_47H_2O$	28·8
(15)	Glycine		2·0
(16)	Meso-inositol		100
(17)	Nicotinic acid		0·5
(18)	Pyridoxine hydrochloride		0·5
(19)	Thiamine hydrochloride		0·1
(20)	IAA		2·0
(21)	Kinetin		0·2
(22)	Sucrose		30 000
	pH 5·8		

Agar 0·6 per cent w/v.

L

Table 6.   An anther culture medium (After J. P. Nitsch and C. Nitsch, based on medium of W. Halperin).

Constituent		Concentration (mg litre⁻¹ medium)
(1) Ammonium nitrate	NH_4NO_3	720
(2) Calcium chloride	$CaCl_2$	166
(3) Magnesium sulphate	$MgSO_47H_2O$	185
(4) Potassium dihydrogen phosphate	KH_2PO_4	68
(5) Potassium nitrate	KNO_3	950
(6) Boric acid	H_3BO_3	10
(7) Copper sulphate	$CuSO_45H_2O$	0·025
(8) Manganese sulphate	$MnSO_44H_2O$	25
(9) Sodium molybdate	$Na_2MoO_42H_2O$	0·25
(10) Zinc sulphate	$ZnSO_47H_2O$	10
(11) Ferric ethylenediamine tetra-acetate	FeEDTA	100*
(12) Biotin		0·05
(13) Folic acid		0·5
(14) Glycine		5·0
(15) Meso-inositol		2·0
(16) Nicotinic acid		0·5
(17) Pyridoxine hydrochloride		0·5
(18) Thiamine hydrochloride		0·5
(19) Sucrose		20 000
pH 5·5		

* FeEDTA solution prepared by dissolving 7·45 g Na_2EDTA and 5·57 g $FeSO_47H_2O$ in 1 litre water.   5 ml is added per litre medium.   Hormones and agar added as required.

Table 7.   Medium for isolated leaf protoplasts of *Nicotiana tabacum* v. *Xanthi*.
(After T. Nagata and I. Takebe).

	Constituent		Concentration (mg per litre medium)
(1)	Ammonium nitrate	NH_4NO_3	825
(2)	Calcium chloride	$CaCl_22H_2O$	220
(3)	Potassium dihydrogen phosphate	KH_2PO_4	680
(4)	Potassium nitrate	KNO_3	950
(5)	Magnesium sulphate	$MgSO_47H_2O$	1233
(6)	Boric acid	H_3BO_3	6·2
(7)	Cobalt sulphate	$CoSO_47H_2O$	0·03
(8)	Copper sulphate	$CuSO_45H_2O$	0·025
(9)	Manganese sulphate	$MnSO_44H_2O$	22·3
(10)	Sodium molybdate	$Na_2MoO_42H_2O$	0·25
(11)	Potassium iodide	KI	0·83
(12)	Zinc sulphate	$ZnSO_44H_2O$	8·60
(13)	Disodium ethylenediamine tetra-acetate	Na_2EDTA	37·3
(14)	Ferrous sulphate	$FeSO_47H_2O$	27·3
(15)	Meso-inositol		100
(16)	Thiamine hydrochloride		1·0
(17)	NAA		3·0
(18)	6-BAP		1·0
(19)	Sucrose		10,000
(20)	Mannitol		13 per cent w/v

pH 5·8

For plating, agar is added at 1·2 per cent w/v and the agar medium diluted with an equal volume of liquid medium containing the protoplasts.

SCHEDULE A. Callus initiation from the basal disc of onion bulb.

(1) Remove the outer scale leaves and the roots of an onion bulb.

(2) Surface sterilize the rest of the bulb in 10 per cent v/v ' Domestos ' bleach (30 min). Rinse thoroughly in sterile water.

(3) Dissect away the scale leaves with a scalpel to expose the bi-convex shaped basal disc.

(4) Cut the basal disc into 2 to 3 mm explants, and lay these on the surface of sterile medium of composition given in Table 4, contained in 100 ml Erlenmeyer flasks or other suitable glass vessels. Use 20 ml of medium in a 100 ml flask. Incubate at 25°C in the dark. Callus begins to appear after about two weeks. Excise callus from the explants after four to six weeks, transfer to the surface of fresh medium, and maintain by regular sub-culture at six week intervals.

(5) Organogenesis by onion callus.
   (*a*) To induce root formation, transfer callus to medium lacking growth hormones.
   (*b*) To induce shoot formation, transfer callus to medium in which 2,4-D (1.0 mg l^{-1}) of the maintenance medium is replaced by NAA (0.1 mg l^{-1}) and 2,i-P (2.0 mg l^{-1}). Incubate in the light (2000 lux). Shoot formation should be induced as soon as possible after callus initiation as the shoot-forming ability of the tissue is lost after four to six months in culture.

SCHEDULE B. A method for the enzymatic isolation of tobacco leaf mesophyll cells. (After I. Takebe, Y. Otsuki, and S. Aoki).

(1) Tobacco plants (*Nicotiana tabacum* v. *Xanthi*) are grown in potting compost in a greenhouse at 25 to 28°C with a 16 h daylength under 11 000 lux illumination provided by banks of ' Daylight ' fluorescent tubes. Expanded leaves are excised for use 60 days after germination.

(2) Surface sterilize excised leaves in 5 per cent v/v ' Domestos ' (30 min). Rinse thoroughly in sterile water.

(3) Remove the lower epidermis by peeling with fine forceps.

(4) Cut regions of exposed mesophyll (about 1 cm square) from the leaves using a scalpel. Incubate 2 g of tissue in 20 ml of filter-sterilized pectinase (0.5 per cent Macerozyme in 13 per cent w/v mannitol; pH adjusted to 5.8 with 2M HCl) in a 100 ml Erlenmeyer flask at 27°C on a reciprocal shaker (100 to 120 cycles/min). (Enzyme supplier: Kinki Yakult Manuf. Co. Ltd., Enzyme products, 8–21 Shingikancho, Nishinomiya, Japan).

(5) Decant enzyme at 30 min intervals over 3 h, replacing with an equal volume of fresh solution at each change. Discard the first enzyme change as this contains cells damaged during peeling of the leaf. Subsequent enzyme aliquots contain viable mesophyll cells. Collect the cells by

156

centrifuging the enzyme $(100 \times g; 5 \text{ min})$ in screw capped centrifuge tubes $(16 \times 125 \text{ mm}$ size are suitable). Bulk cells and wash free of enzyme by resuspending in 13 per cent w/v mannitol solution. Centrifuge, remove supernatant, and resuspend in 13 per cent mannitol.

(6) Determine yield of cells by haemocytometer count.

SCHEDULE C. Enzymatic release of protoplasts from isolated tobacco mesophyll cells. (After Y. Otsuki and I. Takebe).

(1) Prepare mesophyll cells as previously described in Schedule B.

(2) Incubate cells in 50 ml of filter-sterilized cellulase (5 per cent w/v Meicelase in 13 per cent w/v mannitol, pH 5·2) for 3 h at 36°C. (Enzyme supplier: Meiji Seika Kaisha Ltd., 8–2 Chome Kyobashi, Chuo-Ku, Tokyo, Japan).

(3) Collect released protoplasts as a pellet by gentle centrifugation $(100 \times g; 3 \text{ min})$ in screw capped tubes.

(4) Remove enzyme supernatant and resuspend protoplasts in 20 per cent w/v sucrose. Centrifuge $(100 \times g; 5 \text{ min})$. Protoplasts form a layer just below the liquid meniscus.

(5) Remove protoplasts with a pasteur pipette and resuspend in 13 per cent w/v mannitol or liquid culture medium (Table 7). Determine yield of protoplasts by haemocytometer count.

SCHEDULE D. Isolation of protoplasts from tobacco leaf mesophyll and epidermis using a mixed enzyme treatment. (As used in the laboratory of E. C. Cocking).

(1) Peel excised leaves as in Schedule B. Retain the lower epidermis for protoplast isolation.

(2) Excise peeled regions of leaves and place these, exposed mesophyll downwards, on the surface of filter-sterilized enzyme solution (4 per cent w/v Meicelase, 0·4 per cent w/v Macerozyme, in 13 per cent w/v mannitol with the following salts: KH_2PO_4 27·2 mg l^{-1}, KNO_3 101 mg l^{-1}, $CaCl_2 2H_2O$ 1480 mg l^{-1}, $MgSO_4 7H_2O$ 240 mg l^{-1}, KI 0·16 mg l^{-1}, $CuSO_4 5H_2O$ 0·025 mg l^{-1}. The salts are not essential but are beneficial to protoplast viability. Contain the enzyme in petri dishes. Use 15 cm^3 of enzyme in a 90 mm dish, covering the enzyme surface with leaf material. Incubate overnight (18 h) at 25°C.

(3) Gently agitate the leaf pieces with forceps to release the protoplasts.

(4) Transfer the enzyme-protoplast mixture to screw capped tubes, and centrifuge $(100 \times g; 5 \text{ min})$. Mesophyll protoplasts sediment, while those from the upper epidermis float just below the liquid meniscus.

157

(5) Remove the epidermal protoplasts with a pasteur pipette, and wash by resuspending in 13 per cent w/v mannitol solution containing the salts as used in the enzyme. Centrifuge. The epidermal protoplasts again rise to the surface, while mesophyll contaminants sink. Repeat washing procedure. Finally resuspend protoplasts in culture medium (Table 7). Determine yield of upper epidermal protoplasts by haemocytometer count.

(6) Remove remaining enzyme supernatant from above sedimented mesophyll protoplasts. Resuspend and wash mesophyll protoplasts as described in Schedule C. Determine yield of mesophyll protoplasts by haemocytometer count.

(7) The lower epidermis will yield protoplasts when incubated, cuticle uppermost, on the surface of the same enzyme mixture as described in (2). Incubation conditions are the same as in (2). Repeat steps (3) and (4). The lower epidermal protoplasts rise to the surface of the enzyme. Repeat (5), and determine yield of lower epidermal protoplasts.

SCHEDULE E. Culture of isolated tobacco leaf protoplasts.

(*a*) In liquid medium.

(1) Suspend protoplasts in culture medium (Table 7) contained in Erlenmeyer flasks at a density of about $1 \cdot 0 \times 10^5$ protoplasts cm^{-3}. Adjust volume to give a thin layer over the bottom of the culture vessels, e.g. 2 cm^3 in a 25 cm^3 flask, 10 cm^3 in a 250 cm^3 flask. Incubate at 25°C under low intensity fluorescent light (200 lux). Gently swirl the cultures every day to prevent the protoplasts from clumping and adhering to the glass.

(2) After three weeks transfer each culture to a centrifuge tube. Gently centrifuge to pellet the regenerating cells. Remove the old culture medium (supernatant), and replace with an equal volume of fresh medium containing 10 per cent w/v mannitol. Return to incubator. Cells can be gently shaken at this age if a shaker is available.

(3) Repeat (2) after four, five and six weeks, replacing the spent medium with fresh medium containing 5 per cent w/v and 2·5 per cent w/v mannitol respectively. At eight weeks transfer cells to the surface of agar medium given in Table 5.

(*b*) In agar medium.

(1) Suspend protoplasts in liquid culture medium (Table 7) at a density of $2 \cdot 0 \times 10^5$ protoplasts cm^{-3}. Place liquid medium containing protoplasts in a petri dish. Add an equal volume of the same medium containing 1·2 per cent w/v agar at 40°C. Gently swirl to mix and disperse the protoplasts throughout the medium. Allow to set. (Use 3 cm^3 final volume in a 50 mm dish; 10 cm^3 in a 90 mm dish). Incubate (inverted at 25°C under low intensity fluorescent light (200 lux).

(2) After three weeks cut blocks of medium containing dividing regenerated cells from the dishes, and lay the blocks over the surface of fresh agar medium with 10 per cent w/v mannitol. Incubate as in (1).

(3) Repeat (2) after four, five and six weeks with medium containing 5 per cent w/v and 2·5 per cent w/v mannitol respectively. At eight weeks the cell colonies should be above the agar surface. Transfer the colonies to the surface of agar medium given in Table 5.

SCHEDULE F. Organogenesis in tobacco callus initiated from stem explants or derived from isolated leaf protoplasts.

(1) To induce root formation, transfer callus to medium of composition given in Table 5, but with IAA (1·0 mg^{-1}) and kinetin (0·04 mg l^{-1}).

(2) To induce shoot formation, transfer callus to medium of composition given in Table 5, but containing IAA (4·0 mg l^{-1}) and kinetin (2·56 mg l^{-1}). Incubate at 25°C in the light (2000 lux). Adventitious roots can be stimulated to form on the shoots by plunging the base of excised shoots into medium containing NAA (0·1 mg l^{-1}). Rooted plants are subsequently transferred to potting compost, hardened off, and grown to flowering in the greenhouse.

TAXONOMIC INDEX

Bold entry denotes pages with relevant illustration.

161

SUBJECT INDEX

Bold entry denotes pages with relevant illustration.

FURTHER READING

A. TEXT BOOKS

The following books contain articles by scientists in the field of plant tissue culture:

A handbook of plant tissue culture. P. R. White. Ronald Press, New York (1943).

Plant tissue culture and plant morphogenesis. R. G. Butenko. Ed.: M. Kh. Chailakhyan. Translated from Russian by M. Artmann. S. Monson, Jerusalem (1968).

Analysis of growth: the response of cells and tissues in culture. Plant Physiology, Vol. VB; A treatise. Ed.: F. C. Steward. Academic Press, New York and London (1969).

Plant tissue and cell culture. Botanical Monographs, Vol. II. Ed.: H. E. Street. Blackwell Scientific Publications, Oxford (1973).

Tissue culture methods and applications. Ed.: P. F. Kruse and M. K. Patterson. Academic Press, New York and London (1973).

Tissue culture and plant science 1974. Ed.: H. E. Street. Academic Press, New York, London and San Francisco (1974).

Haploids in higher plants. Advances and potential. Proceedings of the First International Symposium, Guelph, Ontario, Canada (1974). Ed.: K. J. Kasha. The University of Guelph, Guelph, Canada (1974).

B. ARTICLES IN SCIENTIFIC JOURNALS

E. C. Cocking. Plant cell protoplasts—isolation and development. *Annual Review of Plant Physiology*, **23,** 29–50 (1972).

W. Halperin. Morphogenesis in cell cultures. *Annual Review of Plant Physiology*, **20,** 395–417 (1969).

M. Hollings. Disease control through virus-free stock. *Annual Review of Phytopathology*, **3,** 367–396 (1965).

A. D. Krikorian and D. L. Berquam. Plant cell and tissue cultures—the role of Haberlandt. *Botanical Review*, **35,** 59–88 (1969).

G. Melchers. Haploid higher plants for plant breeding. *Zeitschrift für Pflanzenzuchtung*, **67,** 19–32 (1972).

T. Murashige. Plant propagation through tissue cultures. *Annual Review of Plant Physiology*, **25,** 135–166 (1974).

H. H. Smith. Model systems for somatic cell genetics. *Bioscience*, **24,** No. 5, 269–276 (1974).

J. G. Torrey. The initiation of organised development in plants. *Advances in Morphogenesis*, **5,** 39–92 (1966).

The books and journals listed are generally available from a science library through inter-library loan.

C. MISCELLANEOUS READING

Embryogenesis in plants. C. W. Wardlaw. Wiley, New York (1955).

The Embryology of Angiosperms. S. S. Bhojwani and S. P. Bhatnagar. Vikas Publishing House, Delhi (1974).

THE WYKEHAM SCIENCE SERIES

THE WYKEHAM TECHNOLOGY SERIES

All orders and requests for inspection copies should be sent to the appropriate agents. A list of agents and their territories is given on the verso of the title page of this book.

† (*Paper and Cloth Editions available.*)